CW00823334

KIWIS

Apteryx australis mantelli
(Bartlett, 1850)

Roa
Apteryx haastii (Potts, 1872)

Apteryx owenii

A MONOGRAPH
OF THE
FAMILY APTERYGIDAE

KIWIS

Editor
Errol Fuller

Text by
J. R. H. Andrews, William A. Calder,
M. A. Fingland, J. N. Jolly, Ruud Kleinpaste,
J. A. McLennan, C. Sinclair Smith

Paintings and Drawings
by
RAY HARRIS-CHING

First published in Great Britain in 1991
by Swan Hill Press.

ISBN 1 85310 220 2

Printed by Everbest Printing Co. Ltd., Hong Kong

Swan Hill Press
An Imprint of Airlife Publishing Ltd
101 Longden Road, Shrewsbury SY3 9EB, England

To Carolyn,
who has shared with me the journeys taken,
both in the studio and other isolated parts of the world,
to bring this book into being.

'. . . although everything in nature is more or less beautiful, every species of object has its own kind and degree of beauty; some being in their own nature more beautiful than others . . .

'Ideas of beauty, then, be it remembered, are the subjects of moral, but not of intellectual perception. By the investigation of them we shall be led to the knowledge of the ideal subjects of art.'

— John Ruskin,
Vol. 1, *Modern Painters*, 1843

Frontispiece
Heads of kiwi species. Brown kiwi, *Apteryx australis*; great spotted kiwi, *Apteryx haastii*; and little spotted kiwi, *Apteryx owenii*. Oil on prepared wood panel, 1987.

North Island brown kiwi, *A. a. mantelli*, on egg in nest chamber in burrow. Oil, 1985.

Contents

Preface

At the Auckland Institute and War Memorial Museum during 1980, when the late Sylvia Reed was curator of the Department of Ornithology, arrangements were made for me to accompany her into the Waitakere Ranges to release a small number of kiwis. The birds had been captured some miles away and removed from an area of forest threatened with felling. They were to be relocated in the Waitakeres, an especially interesting group of high and rugged hills, fringing the western side of the Manukau Harbour and clad in subtropical rainforest.

In a clearing of giant tree ferns, the kiwis were taken, one by one, from the safety of the canvas bags where they had lain, quietly, in the dark, since their capture earlier in the day some hundred miles away. The birds were to be measured, weighed and banded, which inconveniences, not surprisingly, were met with some agitation and an eagerness to be off into the cover of undergrowth. Each kiwi was quickly and expertly handled as the necessary data were gathered, but even so, one smallish male bird showed his displeasure with an angry pink flush brightening up his normally ivory-coloured beak. I had never before seen a kiwi's beak coloured pink — indeed, the entire day was filled with things I didn't know and hadn't seen, and I believe it was then that I resolved to instigate the publication of a volume devoted to these remarkable birds.

But this book really has its beginnings much earlier, in the days that I was able to spend, during the mid-1960s, discovering the wealth of specimens, skeletons and study-skins stored for reference and safekeeping, off the winding corridors of administration and research departments of the Auckland Institute and Museum.

Dr Graham Turbott, then the museum's director, had offered me access to the collections held by the museum, to select and borrow material from which to prepare the paintings of birds that I had fairly recently begun work on. I knew very little about birds, but my deeply felt intent and enthusiasm to produce fine paintings was as intense then as it is now, and, recognising this, the director had extended to me the privilege of borrowing study-skins.

I owe Dr Turbott a very great deal, for, important as it was for me to have skins from which to paint, just as valuable was the wonder and thrill felt each time a store cupboard was opened, a cabinet discovered or a drawer pulled out. Here were kiwis, lying in rows, side by side and on top of each other; brown kiwis and their chicks, great and little spotted kiwis, some collected in recent times, others held in store from the nineteenth century, all with labels tied to their feet containing data of size and sex, colour of eyes, and which part of New Zealand they had been taken from. The opening of another drawer might reveal a series of *Apteryx* eggs, coloured plain white, even rather dull, but not at all commonplace in their huge size and curiously elongated shape.

Times, I'm afraid, have changed in most museums, where directors and staff are no longer able to offer these wonders to a young artist's mind, and skins may no longer be borrowed. It must be my greatest good fortune to

Brown kiwi, *Apteryx australis*. Oil, 1990.

have looked for these things at a time when scientists were rounded men and women, often with visions of glory — able to see the value of faithfully drawing a bird as much for its beauty as for its scientific worth.

Although this volume has its roots amongst the great body of nineteenth-century monographs, I didn't especially require the work to evolve in the same way. The design does not follow the established convention of a single colour plate to represent each species — my own personality wouldn't easily accommodate this restriction — but just as important a force in dictating the book's arrangement and form are the limitations inherent in there being just three kiwi species to portray.

I have, therefore, felt it best to build a visual picture for each species by the accumulative effect of a series of paintings and drawings. For some, I have been able to offer fewer studies than others, a consequence of my having gathered less information from which to structure the plates with certainty. I would, for example, very much like to have included sketches of kiwis mutually preening, as I have heard described, but I lack the confidence to undertake such drawings or paintings, having not seen for myself the birds behaving in this manner.

Perhaps it is worth my saying something here about the materials and techniques used in the making of the paintings. With just the one exception (a watercolour of the North Island brown kiwi and chick), all of the plates are painted in oils, usually on wood panels. For the most part, several coats of gesso form the surface, onto which an elaborate underdrawing of each kiwi is made — mostly from study-skins held in my own studio collection. Although none of this pencil work remains visible on the finished painting, it is nonetheless of first importance that it be both accurate and very detailed. As the work progresses through many layers of paint, this firm, accurate pencil foundation remains an anchor — disallowing major alterations but offering instead a solid position from which to develop and stress points of identification, and at the same time to show the fascinating and often subtle variations between species.

A great many people assisted me in the production of this work — I could not have found the burrows on my own nor seen all of the kiwi species without their guidance.

I have especially to thank Jaan and Dawn Voot for information and reference material, particularly on the Stewart Island subspecies of the brown kiwi. They undertook to travel to this isolated part of the world where the birds live, and they now know, at first hand, the truth of hardships related by nineteenth-century explorers to these lonely islands — especially of the incessant rains that can make life in these wild places so difficult!

My thanks to Bill Double for gathering so much valuable material — largely on the North Island brown kiwi, especially for his efforts to secure details of chicks and burrows from the Hawke's Bay area.

Thanks, too, to Bevan and Loraine Alexander for their valuable help in establishing visual details for the preparation of the plates for the South Island brown kiwi.

At Masons Bay, Senior Ranger Robin Thomas gave much generous assistance and advice in the gathering of reference materials for the plate and drawings of the Stewart Island kiwi.

I want, most particularly, to thank the director and staff at the Otorohanga Zoological Society, where, over a period of years, I made many of the studies on which I based the final paintings, and also the director and staff of the Auckland Zoological gardens for their kind help.

Ray Harris-Ching and Errol Fuller in the studio at Lewes, 1988.

I am indebted to Barry Turner for making available a number of original works in his collection, and to the many people who offered access to paintings and drawings in their possession. The painting of 'North Island Brown Kiwi in Moonlight' that I have used as the species plate is in the collection of the New Zealand Natural Heritage Foundation.

I was very pleased that Errol Fuller was able to edit this volume. He writes regularly on the subject of natural history and has published a study of the birds of paradise and contributed to numerous books and journals. In 1987 he published *Extinct Birds*, an account of the world's recently extinct bird species, which, I am in no doubt, will take its place alongside the classic Rothschild work of 1907.

The authors of the text for this book are formidable field naturalists. From the earliest days of its development, I knew that the contributions must come from leading authorities on specific aspects of *Apteryx* species. I wanted to be able to assemble, in the one book, all that is presently known of these fascinating birds.

J. R. H. Andrews wrote on the discovery of kiwis. Born in Christchurch, New Zealand, in 1940, he obtained a PhD from Victoria University of Wellington and undertook post-doctoral work at the University of Bern. His research fields are medical and veterinary parasitology and the history of zoology, and he is currently reader in biology in the School of Biological Sciences, Victoria University of Wellington, New Zealand. John has contributed a number of scientific publications in his fields of interest, and he is the author of *The Southern Ark*, a history of zoological discovery in New Zealand.

William A. Calder has contributed a chapter on the eggs of the kiwi. Born in Cambridge, Mass., in 1934, he completed US Naval Air Training in 1957 and flew search and rescue and fish and wildlife flights from CGAS, Port Angeles, WA. In 1960 he began graduate studies at Washington State University (MS) and Duke University (PhD). He has taught at Virginia Polytechnic Institute, the Rocky Mountain Biological Laboratory, and is now a professor of ecology and evolutionary biology at the University of Arizona. In 1976 Bill went to New Zealand with some impractical ideas for studying kiwis and was saved from failure by becoming a student of Barry Rowe of the Otorohanga Zoological Society. His main fields of teaching and research have been environmental and comparative physiology, biological scaling, physiological, ecology and environmental science. He is the author of *Size,*

Function and Life History and has contributed ten book chapters and more than 60 articles to biological literature. An NSF grant supported four research projects, including the study from which the chapter in this book was derived.

Martin Fingland wrote on kiwis in aviculture. Born in Plymouth, England, in 1956, Martin emigrated to Australia with his family in 1964. He spent the rest of his childhood growing up in the Dandenong Ranges, near Melbourne, an area rich in wildlife. A career in parks and wildlife management began at the Healesville Sanctuary in Victoria, where Martin worked as a keeper from 1977 to 1982, developing skills with such species as lyrebird and platypus. From 1985 to 1986, he managed the Otorohanga Kiwi House and Wildlife Park in New Zealand, giving him a rare opportunity for study. Notable achievements while there included the breeding of kiwis and tuataras. He is presently senior interpretive officer at Brisbane Forest Park. His articles and photographs have been widely published in geographic and wildlife magazines and journals.

Jim Jolly contributed the text for the little spotted kiwi. He was born in Birmingham, England, in 1944 and moved to New Zealand in 1963. He graduated from Canterbury University in 1974 with an MSc in zoology, completing his thesis on 'Social Behaviour and Habitat Use of the Australian Brush-tailed Possum'. Jim worked as a scientist at the Forest Research Institute from 1974 to 1979, being responsible for research on possum damage on farmland. From 1979 to 1988 he worked for the New Zealand Wildlife Service and the Department of Conservation, with responsibility for research on the ecology, breeding biology and population biology of the little spotted kiwi. His duties included the assessment of suitability of offshore islands for kiwi transfers and the monitoring of transferred birds on Red Mercury and Long Islands. He has published scientific papers and articles for popular publications and books on kiwis, and is now working as a private consultant in wildlife research and conservation education.

Ruud Kleinpaste has written on brown kiwis, specifically in a pine forest habitat. Ruud was born in Indonesia in 1952 and moved to Holland, where he grew up, there developing a keen interest in natural history in general and birds in particular. He studied sylviculture and ecology, with a heavy bias towards conservation, at the Agricultural University, Wageningen. After completing a forestry degree in 1978, Ruud emigrated to New Zealand, where he undertook the research on the brown kiwi that forms the basis of his contribution to this book. He is currently employed by the Ministry of Agriculture and Fisheries in Auckland as an entomologist and has travelled to many countries to study insects.

John McLennan wrote on the brown and the great spotted kiwis. After graduating from Canterbury University with first-class honours in agricultural science in 1973, he joined the Ecology Division, DSIR, later that year to work on starlings and their impact on pasture pests. He was awarded a scholarship in 1976 to study for a PhD at Aberdeen University, and completed his thesis on the flocking behaviour of birds in 1979. On returning to New Zealand, John worked on domestic pigeons, trout and native frogs. He began studies on kiwis in 1982 and has worked full-time on them ever since. His current project is on great spotted kiwis in the mountains of north-west Nelson. He has written various scientific papers and chapters for books on both brown and great spotted kiwis.

Carol Sinclair Smith wrote on the kiwi in art. Born in New Zealand, she now lives in London, where she is a freelance writer and television dramatist. She has written numerous articles on wildlife art and is the author of the book on my work in the series *Masters of the Wild*.

PREFACE

From my studio windows the ground slopes away to a field that rises, steeply wooded on its far side, to the ancient hexagonal ruins of Lewes Castle. The stone archway of the barbican leads to the High Street, and if you turn right, just there on the corner, is the eighteenth-century house lived in by Gideon Mantell.

Gideon it was, who discovered dinosaurs in the Sussex chalk, and it was Gideon who had the first specimen of takahe to reach Europe, on display in his front rooms at that house. Sent to him by his son Walter, who had left Lewes some years earlier for New Zealand, the takahe had been named in Walter's honour, and so has our national bird, for the description of the North Island subspecies of the brown kiwi is *Apteryx australis mantelli*.

Ray Harris-Ching
Lewes, 1989

Drawn Engraved & Published by R. Nodder.

1

A HISTORY OF KIWI DISCOVERY

It can be reasonably argued that no bird has stood for so much in the New Zealand context as the kiwi. It was highly prized by the Maoris, a profound source of fascination to nineteenth-century naturalists and, more recently, a national symbol whose name has become synonymous with the people who inhabit its country. Yet, all the while, the bird has been a relatively secretive, nocturnal species, seldom seen in the wild state by the human population that holds it in such high esteem.

Before the coming of Europeans, the Maoris sought kiwis for food and made up the skins and feathers into cloaks. They hunted the birds at night with the aid of dogs and torches: so successfully that by the time James Cook and his naturalists arrived in New Zealand in 1769, hunting and habitat destruction had already substantially reduced kiwi numbers and the feathered cloaks were increasingly scarce.

European science, as represented by Banks, Solander and the other members of Cook's scientific contingent, were apparently not aware of the kiwi's existence, although they might have unwittingly seen the bird's feathers as part of a cloak or some other adornment. Their restriction to coastal exploration and the limitations of communication with the Maoris would not have increased their chances of seeing a kiwi intact. Thus the bird was to remain unknown to these and other European visitors until more than 40 years had passed.

APTERYX AUSTRALIS AUSTRALIS
THE SOUTH ISLAND BROWN KIWI

It was in 1813 that the first formal notice of a kiwi discovery appeared. This took the form of a written description and illustrations of the bird, and came in what was to be the final volume of a natural history series entitled *The Naturalist's Miscellany*. The series was devised and written by George Shaw, the ebullient keeper of zoology in the British Museum, and illustrated by Frederick Nodder, whose experience in natural history illustration included some early work on the botanical specimens collected on Cook's first voyage to New Zealand. Nodder died shortly before the work on the kiwi commenced, and his place was taken by his wife, Elizabeth, and his son, R. P. Nodder. Shaw himself was to die shortly after the volume containing the kiwi appeared.

It is Shaw's original description that provides us with a starting point for an investigation of the history of kiwi discovery by European naturalists. The

The first published picture of a kiwi. Hand-coloured engraving by R. P. Nodder for Vol. 24 of G. Shaw and F. Nodder's *The Naturalist's Miscellany* (London, 1813).

original specimen, which has been preserved as a skin, provides very little in the way of clues either to its discovery or its precise geographic origin. Fortunately, Shaw was fairly detailed in his description of the bird itself and how he had come by it, and it is there that we must look for pointers to this information. The following extracts are from his original description:

> The bird represented on the present plate constitutes a perfectly new genus, which it is not easy to refer to any of the established ornithological orders. It seems however to approach more nearly to the Struthious and the Gallinaceous tribes than to any other, though the very different form of the beak implies a different manner of life . . . the plumage bears a strong alliance to that of the brown or New Holland Cassowary. The head is rather small, and the neck of moderate length; the legs, which are situated as in the Penguins, are short and strong. . . . There is no appearance of a tail, and in place of wings (unless any art of deception has been practised, of which I cannot discover the least appearance) can only be perceived a small single joint on each side . . . The colour of the whole bird is ferruginous . . . This curious bird is a native of New Zealand, from the south coast of which it was brought by Captain Barcley [*sic*] of the *Providence*, by whom, through the kind interposition of my friend, W. Evans, Esq., it was presented to myself.

The description, in English, was preceded by one in Latin, as was customary, headed by the Latin binomial that became the formal name for the species: thus *Apteryx australis* — the southern *Apteryx* — came into being. Until this day the name has stood unchanged, having survived differing opinions and challenges by ornithologists of this century and the last — a credit to Shaw, both for his determination of the bird's position in avian systematics and the quality of its description. Unfortunately, Shaw's tenure of the keepership of zoology at the British Museum was not always marked by such good judgement.

The only weakness in this first description of the kiwi was the representation of the bird in one of R. P. Nodder's engravings. Years later, experienced preparers of bird skins and bird illustrators could perform miracles with a dried or preserved skin, and come up with a relatively life-like rendition of the original. But earlier, there was a more limited knowledge of the shapes that birds could attain, and in the probable absence of any accompanying information, Shaw and the young Nodder had to proceed with a somewhat distorted dried skin, with the result that they put the kiwi in a very peculiar pose. However, a second engraving, showing detail of beak, feathers and feet, was beyond reproach.

In part, it was probably their rendering of the external features of the kiwi that led to later ornithologists attempting to classify it with the penguins (assisted, no doubt by Shaw's references to penguins in the written description). The situation was not helped by the fact that many years were to pass before another specimen was obtained or reliable reports as to the bird's appearance were circulated.

Returning again to the question of the kiwi's discovery: mention of Captain Barclay ('Barcley' in Shaw's text), the *Providence*, 'W. Evans, Esq.', as well as the 'south coast' of New Zealand, provides some basis for further investigation. It seems that Captain Barclay was a privateer who, with the *Providence*, was engaged in transporting convicts to Australia, as well as carrying general cargoes. At about the time the kiwi was presumed to have been discovered (we must allow a year or two prior to Shaw's publication in 1813), Barclay and his vessel can be pinpointed at Port Jackson (Sydney) between 2 July and 20 October 1811. It can be assumed that he proceeded

Captain Barclay's kiwi. Now in the Liverpool Museum, this historic specimen was taken to England during 1812.
Courtesy of National Museums and Galleries on Merseyside (Liverpool Museum)

directly to Sydney, as he was carrying 174 convicts and 36 soldiers as well as some general cargo, and would not have detoured to New Zealand at that stage. His return to England was apparently by way of China, where he picked up a load of tea. Again a detour to New Zealand seems unlikely. Although there was a seal-skin trade with China at the time, there is no evidence of his having gone to New Zealand to collect them (in any event, such a cargo would most likely have been picked up from Sydney, where the sealing companies were based) and he is recorded as leaving Sydney under ballast. Barclay's own reminiscences, published many years later, are not helpful on these points.

This interpretation leaves us with circumstantial evidence that suggests Barclay was offered the kiwi skin while he was enjoying his three-month stay in Sydney. The original collectors may well have been sealers stationed in the Stewart Island-Foveaux Strait area (the focus of sealing activity at that time), and two vessels had not long since relieved sealing parties before returning to Sydney (*Boyd*, 26/3/1811, and *Sydney Cove*, 13/4/1811). Trading in natural history specimens was common at the time, and seafarers of all kinds were aware of the potential value of anything that was at all exotic or unusual; sealers in particular were implicated in a number of important natural history transactions during the nineteenth century.

Barclay arrived back in England on 15 May 1812, and only a relatively short time must have elapsed before the kiwi skin, through the mediation of the mutual friend W. Evans (about whom nothing more is known at present), was presented to George Shaw, who described it as related above.

After Shaw's death the specimen went, in the sale of his personal effects, to Lord Stanley (the Earl of Derby) a well-known collector of animals, both alive and dead, as well as other items of natural history interest. Although he maintained what was virtually a private menagerie, museum and library, he performed a public service by providing one of those useful focal points for natural history specimens at a time when the public museums were still finding their feet.

Apart from the occasional outing — on loan to the Zoological Society of London, for example — the bird remained in the Liverpool area, where the Derby estates are located, until the present day. It is now to be found in the Liverpool Museum, where much of the Derby collection was deposited during the last century. The kiwi skin still has some Derby labels attached to it, but there is no trace of reference to its previous ownership, nor is there any reference to the locality of its collection other than the fact that it came from New Zealand. The manuscript that accompanies the Derby collection is equally unhelpful. It was later said by A. D. Bartlett (quoting J. E. Gray, a later keeper of zoology at the British Museum) that this kiwi had come from 'Dusky Bay' — but this may simply have been an assumption on Gray's part, as he would have been aware that a number of other zoological specimens from early New Zealand had come from this particular location.

After Shaw had described the kiwi, other ornithologists re-evaluated his description, and came to different conclusions about its relationships. The eminent English ornithologist John Latham called it an 'apterous penguin' and C. J. Temminck, in Amsterdam, placed the kiwi with the dodo. However, these were aberrations and the place of the kiwi in the Order Apterygiformes of the Ratitae has long been acknowledged — although it is interesting to note that as recently as 1960 a claim was made that the kiwi was distantly allied to penguins. Shaw's kiwi was finally designated *Apteryx australis australis*, the South Island brown kiwi — for some time the only species of kiwi that was recognised.

APTERYX AUSTRALIS MANTELLI
THE NORTH ISLAND BROWN KIWI

Part of the perplexity surrounding early understanding of the kiwi was due to the fact that only the scantiest of sightings and records followed Shaw's description, and it was to be many years before another specimen reached Europe. Those reports that did come to hand were published in volumes of the sort that were less likely to be scrutinised by ornithologists. A visitor to the North Island of New Zealand in 1814–15, J. L. Nicholas, detected the relationships of the kiwi entirely on the basis of the structure of feathers seen on some Maori cloaks — a surprising feat by someone who would have claimed that he had no particular skills or interest in natural history. A similar observation was made by Major Richard Cruise, although he was probably in a position to be informed by the missionaries, who were by then well established and were aware of the bird and its means of capture by the Maoris.

The early scattered reports of a kiwi in the North Island in no way indicated that the bird was different from the one described by Shaw, and part of the future difficulty in establishing that there was in fact a difference would lie in the problem of supplying specimens from both the North and South Islands, and being able to compare them.

It was to be some years before naturalists in England were to be faced with the first whole specimen of a North Island brown kiwi. In the meantime, a tantalising fragment fell into the hands of R. P. Lesson, the French naturalist on board the *Coquille*, which visited New Zealand in 1824. The exact nature of the kiwi material that Lesson took back to France is unknown and no trace of it remains today, but it was possibly part of a skin. It was enough for Lesson to recognise the affinity of the bird with the Australian emu, but not sufficient to identify it as the kiwi described by Shaw. Accordingly, he described it as *Dromiceius novaezelandiae*, a name that is no longer accepted. But he did introduce the Maori name 'kiwi' to Europe. The French learned a little more about the kiwi when Dumont d'Urville visited Tolaga Bay in February 1827 on board the *Astrolabe*, but sighting of the bird had yet to progress beyond the stage of viewing kiwi-skin cloaks.

Then, in response to an appeal by the Zoological Society of London,

North Island brown kiwi, *Apteryx australis mantelli*. Chromolithograph by J. G. Keulemans from W. L. Buller's *History of the Birds of New Zealand* (London, 1888).

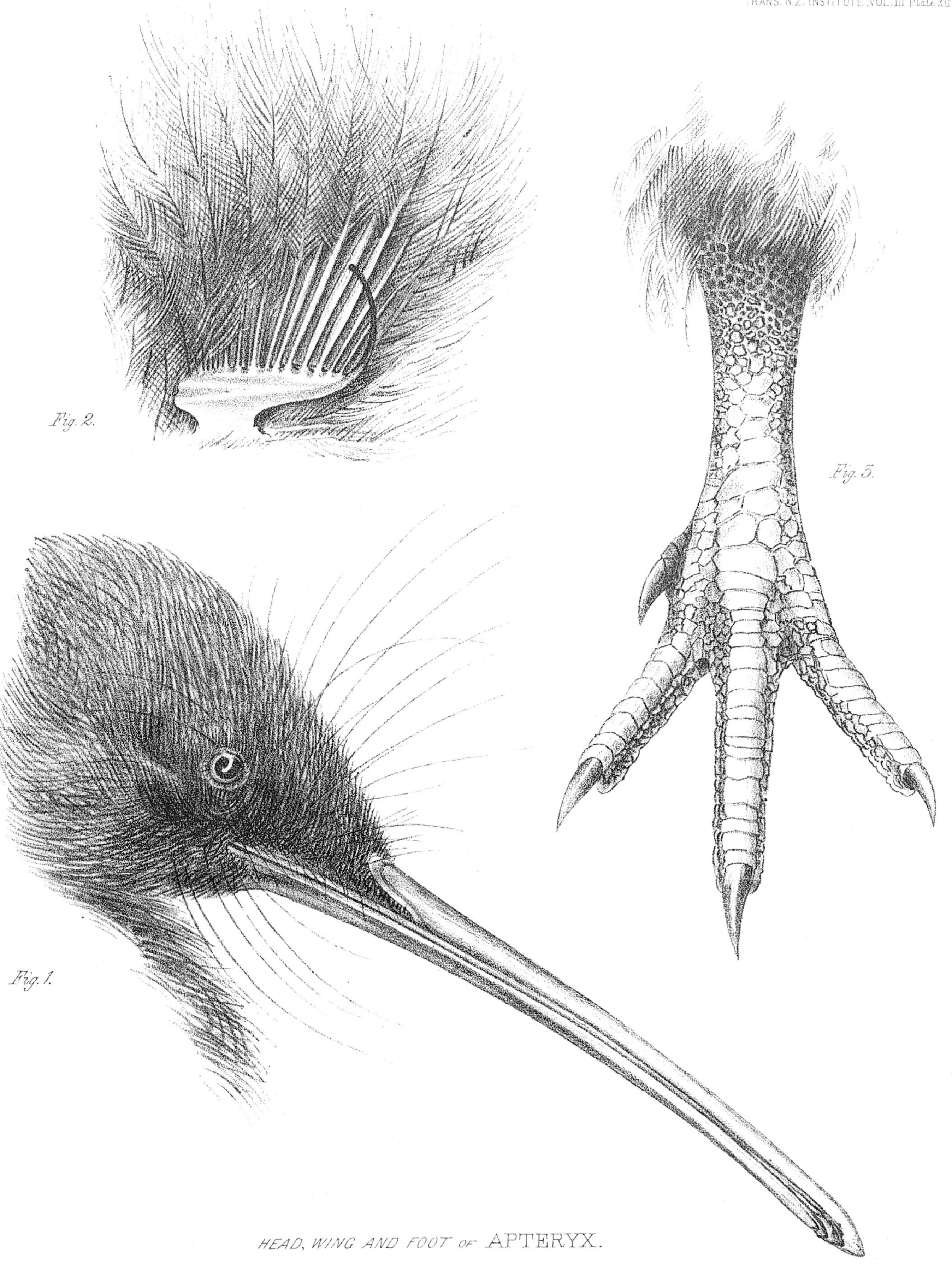

HEAD, WING AND FOOT OF APTERYX.

W. Buller del. J.B. lith.

Printed at the Gen. Gov. Lith. Press, by J. Earle.

Alexander Macleay (the Colonial Secretary of New South Wales) made contact with one of the Bay of Islands missionaries, requesting a specimen. His contact, the Reverend William Yate, was a fortunate choice, as he was one of the first missionaries to make a study of New Zealand's natural history. At about the time of Macleay's request, Yate had a live North Island brown kiwi in captivity; but fate was to deny European science its first good look at an entire bird. It died while Yate was temporarily absent on pastoral duties, and only the skin was saved.

Other kiwis, possibly from the North Island, reached England during the 1830s. These went to the Earl of Derby or Richard Owen, for his anatomical studies, rather than to taxonomists, but in time a steady supply of North Island birds was established. Comparison of birds from the North and South Islands was, however, still difficult to accomplish and it was not until the ornithologist from the Zoological Society of London, A. D. Bartlett, was confronted simultaneously with specimens from both localities that any differences were noted. The opportunity arose when he was handed a specimen by Dr Gideon Mantell, well known for his palaeontological work, whose son Walter was living in New Zealand. Walter Mantell supplied his father with an abundance of natural history material, some of which had great significance for New Zealand ornithology. This particular kiwi had been taken at 'Dusky Bay' and was noted by Bartlett to be different to a number of specimens that he was able to bring in from the British Museum and the Royal College of Surgeons, and from the Zoological Society's own collections. To be certain of his judgement, he borrowed the Earl of Derby's specimen, to find that it and the Mantell bird were the same, but that the others that had been filling their collections were of a different kind. As a result of this discovery, Bartlett declared that the North Island birds were to belong to a new species, *Apteryx mantelli*, one that was later, after much scientific debate, relegated to a subspecies, *Apteryx australis mantelli*.

Gideon Mantell, *c.* 1830.

Walter Mantell, *c.* 1870.

APTERYX OWENII
THE LITTLE SPOTTED KIWI

Although specimens of the North Island brown kiwi had been arriving in England for some years, it was not in fact the second form of kiwi to be described by ornithologists. That distinction went to a bird that was apparently quite common in those earlier years but is now quite rare — the little spotted kiwi, *Apteryx owenii*. Not a great deal is known about the early discovery of this bird, but an individual appears to have been caught by sealers (or their dogs) and taken to Sydney, where it was sold to a professional natural history dealer by the name of Frederick Strange. Through Strange, it was sold to the ornithologist and bird illustrator John Gould, who published its description in 1847, with an illustration appearing in his *Birds of Australia* the following year. The species was named after Richard Owen, who had so much to do with describing the anatomy of kiwis. Several unsuccessful attempts have since been made to assign *A. owenii* to a new genus.

Although the little spotted kiwi was probably described from the South Island, a reliable record was later made from the North Island as a result of the capture, by dogs, of a bird on Mount Hector in the Tararua Ranges. Morgan Carkeek, who obtained it for the ornithologist Walter Buller, noted that there were a number of others above and below the snowline. It was a record that puzzled Buller, leading him to think that the little spotted kiwi did not occur there naturally and had been introduced from the South Island (see below). However, the discovery of subfossil bones throughout the North Island is

Head, wing and foot of *Apteryx*. Lithograph by J. Earle. Walter Buller, *Apteryx australis* from *Transactions of the New Zealand Institute*, Vol. III, 1870, Plate XIIb.

Little spotted kiwi, *Apteryx owenii*. Hand-coloured lithograph by J. Gould and H. C. Richter from J. Gould's *Birds of Australia* (London, 1840–69).

ample evidence of its former New Zealand-wide distribution. Whatever its origins, the little spotted kiwi did not last much longer in the North Island and became increasingly uncommon in the South.

APTERYX HAASTII
THE GREAT SPOTTED KIWI

All the kiwis so far described had been sent by collectors and others to England, where the appropriate institutions and expertise resided, for their description. At the time of the earlier discoveries, no comparable New Zealand facilities existed that would provide for the bird's published description and its curation. Even Australia, with its fledgling scientific institutions, was little better developed than New Zealand in this respect, although the Tasmanian Natural History Society and its journal attracted contributions from New Zealand.

Natural history collectors and their agents who were domiciled in New Zealand or Australia were often committed, either through family or commercial ties, to supplying individuals or institutions back in England, and it was not until their local scientific counterparts had established themselves that the direction of the flow was changed and significant zoological material was described in New Zealand. Thus it was that the last two kiwis to be discovered and named were described in this way.

Great spotted kiwi, *Apteryx haastii*, and chick. Hand-coloured lithograph by J. G. Keulemans from G. D. Rowley's *Ornithological Miscellany* (London, 1875–78).

½

Julius von Haast, *c.* 1885.

The first of these was a bird whose reputation preceded it, as apparently both the bird and its eggs were larger than those previously described. Sealers called this bird the 'Fireman' — why, it is not quite clear. The term has been used in the past to describe one who went down mines in order to extinguish a fire — which might be a rather oblique reference to the kiwi's habit of living in holes or chambers in the ground, or its call. Knowledge of this bird's existence came to the Sydney dealer Frederick Strange, who passed on the information to John Gould, but he was unable to obtain a specimen.

In the end it was the notorious bird collector William Docherty who was the source of two examples, included with a consignment of bird skins to the Christchurch naturalist Thomas Henry Potts. A male was said to have been caught between Lake Mapourika and the main range and a female was found in bush some distance up the Okarito River. Potts described these kiwis in the *Transactions and Proceedings of the New Zealand Institute* in 1872. The bird was named *Apteryx haastii* in honour of the director of the Canterbury Museum, Julius von Haast, who had earlier detected footprints believed to have been made by this species. The name and status of this kiwi have remained unchanged until the present day, and the original specimens remain in the Canterbury Museum.

APTERYX AUSTRALIS LAWRYI
THE STEWART ISLAND KIWI

The last kiwi to be described was one from Stewart Island, and was exhibited by Walter Buller at a meeting of the Wellington Philosophical Society on 2 July 1890. In giving this rather large specimen a name, he made reference to a note written in 1856 by Charles Lucien Bonaparte which mentioned, by name only, a large kiwi called *Apteryx maxima*. The author of this name was apparently Jules Verreaux, who was a member of a family business based in Paris which dealt in natural history specimens, and who visited New Zealand on collecting expeditions. Verreaux's name for this bird was unaccompanied by a description, and the specimen had disappeared, so the name had no scientific status. Accordingly, the name used by Buller was changed by Walter Rothschild in 1893 to *Apteryx lawryi*. Since then there has been some doubt about the separate specific status of the Stewart Island bird, and the name has been amended to *Apteryx australis lawryi*, allying the form to the South Island brown kiwi but giving it a distinctive identity at subspecific level.

Walter Rothschild was a prominent English ornithologist, with a large number of kiwis in his private collection. In 1899 he published a substantial paper entitled 'The Genus *Apteryx*', which carried some notes on the anatomy of the kiwis by F. E. Beddard. Apart from *A. lawryi* and a new subspecies of *A. owenii* created by Rothschild and called *occidentalis*, all species mentioned by Rothschild are valid today. Thus, by the end of the nineteenth century kiwi taxonomy had more or less stabilised.

Walter Rothschild, *c.* 1895.
Courtesy of the Hon. Miriam Rothschild

KIWI ANATOMY AND DEVELOPMENT

Discovery and description of the various kinds of kiwis marked only a beginning. A number of investigations awaited a growing force of biologists whose attention was rapidly being drawn to new or growing branches of the science. Comparative anatomy, behaviour, ecology, developmental zoology, evolution and biogeography were among those to emerge or make rapid advances during the nineteenth century, and any species that was discovered as being at all out of the ordinary was promptly conscripted for such studies.

A HISTORY OF KIWI DISCOVERY

It was comparative anatomy that was in its ascendancy at the time of kiwi discovery, with the French school under Cuvier becoming predominant. However, early attempts to procure kiwis by members of the French voyages of exploration under Duperrey and Dumont d'Urville were unsuccessful, and by the time one became available, in 1840, interest in what lay underneath the feathers was restricted to a published illustration of the skeleton. Instead, it became the turn of the English to broach the kiwi anatomy, with material support from colonial contacts and a rising tide of enthusiasm for comparative anatomy under the leadership of Richard Owen. Owen's progression from the Royal College of Surgeons to the Natural History Museum was marked by a vast influx of specimens from a growing number of British colonies, and his domination of comparative anatomical science ensured that a large part of that cornucopia went in his direction.

Sir Richard Owen, *c.* 1880.

In March 1838, Owen was supplied with a kiwi that had come via Lord Derby to the Zoological Society of London. This opened the way for an important series of anatomical studies that began in June of that year. He was still engaged on this bird during November, but in 1839 he was in a position to report his findings to the Zoological Society of London, with an illustrated account emerging the following year. His work was given further impetus when three specimens arrived from Walter Mantell, early in the 1840s.

The time taken for Owen to process the first bird reflects the volume of material that clamoured for attention, and his busy social and professional schedule. It also explains why he sometimes made mistakes, none more embarrassing than his confusing of the heart of a duck-billed platypus with that of a kiwi. This slip-up was politely drawn to public attention by Professor E. R. Lankester in 1885, a good many years after the event. Owen published a vigorous denial, but a rebuttal by Lankester clearly demonstrated that the former's memory did not serve him well, and Owen was finally reduced to silence.

Although other notable Victorian scientists made contributions to the anatomical study of kiwis (Thomas Huxley, for example), Owen's studies were by far the most comprehensive. However, his preoccupation with palaeontology and more static anatomy gave him fewer opportunities to publish on the juvenile stages, although he did write a paper on kiwi eggs. Thus the field of the kiwi's developmental biology was virtually wide open when Thomas Jeffery Parker (who became professor of zoology at the University of Otago) began to enquire into it. Parker wrote several papers on kiwi anatomy, but it was his work on the embryonic development of the skeleton and skull that was particularly significant. He was aided in the collection of specimens by Richard Henry, who was caretaker of a bird sanctuary at Resolution Island in Dusky Sound, as well as Walter Buller, F. W. Hutton and James Hector. Parker's work on the brain and its development was not further advanced until the work of Craigie, Durward and Krabbe appeared later in the twentieth century.

KIWI ORIGINS AND RELATIONSHIPS

Aside from the inevitable disagreements over the validity of the various species of kiwi described in New Zealand (between the German ornithologist Otto Finsch and his English counterparts, for example), a body of discussion arose over their origins, evolution and relationships. It was inevitable that there would be statement and speculation on these matters, and discussion as to how these birds had evolved and had continued to survive in a southern portion of the globe.

Forbes Co. Boston.

Discoveries of the anatomists, such as those by Richard Owen, provided the resource for further and more detailed comparisons with birds from other groups. Other prominent nineteenth-century naturalists, such as St George Mivart and Thomas Huxley, joined the debate, the former's contribution to kiwi relationships being particularly far-sighted. Mivart had grouped the Australian, New Guinean and New Zealand ratites, relating them to another group, consisting of South American and African representatives — a view that was much later confirmed by DNA-DNA hybridisation techniques and parasitological evidence. But, predictably, it was the New Zealand scientific establishment that was to provide the most substantial contribution in the area of origins and relationships: not least because they had the best overview of the fauna and the closest understanding of New Zealand's geological history, which they could blend with the recently emergent views of biological evolution generated by Darwin and Wallace. No longer was it necessary to make broad biological generalisations on a suite of stuffed specimens viewed half a world away from their natural location.

Sir Walter Lawry Buller, *c.* 1900.

In one of the early published statements on the origins and evolution of the New Zealand fauna, Frederick Wollaston Hutton provided a basis for future discussion of specific groups such as kiwis. He dealt, fairly broadly, with the origins of the flightless birds, particularly the moas. But he did reserve some remarks for the kiwis, saying that they were an older group than the other 'Struthiones' and had preserved some carinate affinities. He presented a further paper on this subject to the Australasian Association for the Advancement of Science in 1892. Hutton's theories were later built on by Buller in a paper in which he saw the kiwis and their relatives as descendants (in other words, degenerate forms) of flying birds that had become united on the islands of New Zealand following geological submergence and upheaval. Natural selection operated to give the species of kiwi now present. Buller had some bother with the contemporary presence of *A. owenii* in both islands of New Zealand, which he attempted to account for by suggesting that Maoris transported the bird from the South Island.

Modern views on the origins, evolution and distribution of kiwis and their relatives have since overtaken the theories of Buller and Hutton. In the light of current knowledge of continental drift, electrophoretic techniques, new theories of phylogenetics and biogeography, and a better understanding of faunas in general, some of their speculations may now seem a little quaint.

DISTRIBUTION AND CONSERVATION

Although current distribution and conservation will be discussed in detail elsewhere in this volume, it is worth recording the impressions that kiwi distribution and the status of their populations made on the early collectors. Of even greater significance is the early recognition of a general decline in kiwi numbers, and the need for their preservation and conservation.

Collectors, dogs, habitat destruction and introduced predators have variously contributed to changes in kiwi distribution. Early published works document the decline in a fairly coarse fashion: a reduction in numbers here, an apparent absence of birds there. Accurate determinations of numbers and distribution were beyond the resources of most of those early observers, and even today no clear reason has been established for the rarity of *A. australis australis* outside of Fiordland and Okarito.

In pre-European times, some general indication of the localised scarcity of the kiwi can be gained from the growing rarity of kiwi-skin cloaks worn by the Maoris and the infrequency of kiwi bones in Maori middens. The cloaks

South Island brown kiwi, *Apteryx australis*, a nineteenth-century lithograph.

were highly prized and usually belonged to persons of rank. European collection of kiwi skins accelerated greatly in the latter half of the nineteenth century in response to a fashion for kiwi-skin muffs and requests from museums and private collectors abroad. These developments encouraged the activities of 'professional' collectors, a mixture of surveyors and men with hermit-like tendencies who sometimes lacked the skills or resources necessary to place kiwi observations in the permanent scientific record. In any event, it was not until the *Transactions and Proceedings of the New Zealand Institute* began publication in 1869 that any formal means existed by which such records could be kept. Prior to this time, the published records of the New Zealand fauna were usually restricted to works published overseas, journals such as the *Proceedings of the Zoological Society of London*. Such organs were largely beyond the reach of those who laboured in the New Zealand bush, but in due course the collectors became associated with the developing university and museum network as well as the band of informed amateur naturalists that came to inhabit this country.

From the earliest times the records of kiwis by Europeans have tended as much to reflect the distribution and activities of the human population as they did the birds themselves. The very first record probably resulted from the presence of sealers in the southern South Island. Thereafter came a spate of records from the North Island, as the population settled and grew there. Then, with more widespread development, exploration and mining, records from the South Island were renewed — particularly from the West Coast and Fiordland areas.

With a small network of collectors serving both overseas and, eventually, local interests, it was inevitable that some of their observations on the distribution or decline of kiwi populations would find their way directly or indirectly into the published record. For example, in the *Transactions and Proceedings of the New Zealand Institute* of 1877 (published 1878) we learn that very few specimens of *A. a. australis* were being brought in by collectors but that the supply of *A. owenii* was undiminished.

The increasing scarcity of *A. a. australis* relative to *owenii* was referred to again in the same journal in 1885. Although the former was to be found from Dusky Sound through to Jacksons Bay, it was annually becoming less widely distributed, while *owenii*, less common in the Fiordland Sounds, favoured the higher and drier areas. In the same journal, during the following year, it was noted that all species of kiwi were becoming rare, especially *A. a. australis* and *A. haastii*.

Meanwhile, in the North Island there was a singular sighting of *A. owenii* made at Mount Hector in the Tararua Ranges by Morgan Carkeek in 1875, and reported in the *Transactions* by Walter Buller. It was a valuable record, for this species disappeared from the North Island shortly thereafter. Strangely, the North Island brown kiwi, *A. australis mantelli*, was not frequently mentioned, although Buller noted that it was still plentiful in the Kaimanawa Ranges in 1877, and as late as 1892, good numbers were still being obtained south of New Plymouth. There are a number of other brief references to the distribution of this and the other kiwi species in the copious notes published by Buller in successive issues of the *Transactions and Proceedings of the New Zealand Institute*.

A steadily recurring theme in the published records was the retrenchment of the numbers and distribution of these birds. This was attributable to a variety of causes, directly or indirectly of human origin and mentioned elsewhere in this chapter. Commercial and scientific interest in the kiwi placed humans as both agents of destruction and salvation. Given the environment in

Andreas Reischek, *c.* 1895.

which the birds were to be found, and the effort required to catch them, it is perhaps not surprising to find that a number of those involved with handling kiwis in the field were of a particular profile. They were solitary, hard-bitten men, clearly capable of putting up with enormous hardships in the most demanding of landscapes. Some of them even showed genuine affection and concern for the wildlife that they bagged — a familiar contradiction in the history of nineteenth-century science. Later, and with the growing realisation of the damage being done to the native fauna, one or two of the poachers turned gamekeeper, signalling an end to the rapacity that had gone before.

T. H. Potts, *c.* 1870.

Among the earliest of the 'professional' collectors was William Docherty, a prospector and animal collector who had been in the south since the 1860s. He had been prospecting and collecting in the Haast region before moving north to Okarito, where in 1868 he met up with Julius von Haast, the provincial geologist for Canterbury, later to be director of the Canterbury Museum. It was Haast who taught Docherty the technique of preserving bird skins and then became, on behalf of the museum, one of Docherty's most reliable customers. It was Docherty who sent the first skins of *A. haastii* to Thomas Henry Potts, who did not name his collector but described him as one who had 'slain his thousands of Apterygidae' and had supplied a number of foreign museums. Early in 1877, Docherty moved south to Dusky Sound, where he spent seventeen years before spending his last days at Preservation Inlet.

Samuel Percy Seymour was another hermit collector, but with the distinction that he obtained a BA from Otago University before heading for Doubtful Sound in 1886 to begin the life of an animal collector, including kiwis among his stock. His principal client was a Mr Marsden of Gloucester, but he corresponded with (and collected for) Professors Parker and Benham of the Otago University and Museum, both of whom published works on kiwis. It was Seymour's hope that he would one day produce a book on the fauna of the area, but only the odd scientific note materialised. Early in his stay at Doubtful Sound, Seymour had seen *A. australis* but no sign of *A. owenii*. Later, however, he reported to Buller on the breeding intervals of the latter species.

An itinerant figure in the midst of these hermit collectors was the Austrian-born Andreas Reischek. A solitary figure, often with only his dog for company, Reischek was a field naturalist of unalloyed enthusiasm. His dedication allowed him to make many useful observations on the New Zealand fauna, a number of which were published in the *Transactions*. Unfortunately, his record has been marred by a reputation for over-zealous shooting of birds, including species that were rare. He makes nothing of whipping the skin off a kiwi while at the same time noting features of its environment, behaviour or anatomy in scrupulous detail. He was fundamentally a collector and would spare no effort to track specimens down. This example, involving *A. owenii* is typical: 'With the assistance of my dog it sometimes took me half a day to secure a bird, and very often I had to give up without result.' In the course of his visits to Fiordland he encountered some of the other collectors, and spent some time with William Docherty at Dusky Sound in 1884.

Although the men just described were useful sources of scientific information on kiwis and other birds, they were part of a growing focus of disapproval, by naturalists and others, which culminated in attempts at conservation and preservation of some of the species they were collecting. Recognition of the problem was frequently made by the collectors themselves: destruction of habitat, the increase of existing predators and the introduction of new ones were seen to have grave import for ground birds such as the kiwi. Even activities such as gold mining were recognised as having an impact on the environment. But it was the naturalists themselves who sounded the earliest warnings — T. H. Potts, for example, who used the second volume of the *Transactions*, in 1870, to publicise his concern over the decline of the kiwi and kakapo, with a plea for government intervention. Plans to introduce mustelids (ferrets, stoats and weasels) to control rabbits were greeted with further alarm by the naturalists and spurred on the efforts of the collectors to acquire even more specimens of rare birds before they disappeared. In fact the mustelids may well have done less damage than commonly supposed, and even Walter Buller pointed out that not everything could be blamed on these animals, but in those days a lack of ecological understanding forced naturalists back on an instinctive evaluation of the situation. In spite of numerous pleas (including those from the English ornithologist Professor Alfred Newton), the mustelids were released. In 1886 the Animals Protection Act was amended to prohibit the killing of any indigenous bird species that was notified in the *New Zealand Gazette*. The kiwi, along with several other birds, was gazetted in 1896. By then much of the damage was done, and although the legislation presumably curtailed the activities of collectors, it would have had little effect on predators.

With the introduction and spread of mustelids, calls were made to establish island reserves for the wingless birds, a proposal that was encouraged by the Governor, Lord Onslow. In due course an island reserve for the protection of kiwis and other flightless birds of the Fiordland region was established at Resolution Island, Dusky Sound, and in July 1894 its first curator and caretaker arrived at Pigeon Island nearby.

Richard Henry, ex-rabbiter, jack-of-all-trades and naturalist, was based at Lake Te Anau, from where he explored the Fiordland region and collected, and presumably sold, bird specimens. During his time in Dusky Sound he caught birds, including kiwis, with the aid of a muzzled dog that carried a bell around its neck, and transported the birds to Resolution Island and other islands in the Sound. To begin with, Resolution Island held only *A. a. australis* and no *A. owenii*, but in time a number of the latter and some kakapos were thriving in their new location. Henry stayed on in Dusky Sound until 1908, leaving it in the knowledge that mustelids had invaded his sanctuary and the prognosis for the survival of the birds was not good. He removed to Kapiti Island, another sanctuary, where kiwis were later successfully introduced. Resulting from his observations of bird life in Dusky Sound, Henry made several written contributions to the *Transactions and Proceedings of the New Zealand Institute* and published a book entitled *The Habits of the Flightless Birds of New Zealand*.

Transfer of birds to offshore islands continued to be a favoured means of preserving kiwis, the attempt to establish the rarer *A. haastii* on Little Barrier Island in 1915 being an example.

BEHAVIOUR

In an introductory statement on the brown kiwi, accompanying a 1967 reprint of Walter Buller's *A History of the Birds of New Zealand*, the ornithologist E. G. Turbott wrote, 'It is indeed surprising that comparatively little field study has yet been devoted to this remarkable group: the field notes and observations of kiwis in captivity recorded by Buller still form our main source of information!' Buller, like a number of other nineteenth-century naturalists, kept kiwis in captivity and was able to comment at some length on their breeding behaviour and biology.

Buller's observations were made mostly from captured specimens, although an occasional kiwi hunt provided him with an opportunity to observe some of their breeding behaviour in the wild, as well as their food preferences. His observation of feeding behaviour in captive birds was enhanced by the use of a phosphorescent worm, which made the movements of the bird and its prey visible at night — the time of greatest activity. Whether this 'experiment' was the result of accident or design is not disclosed. It is interesting that Buller's evident enthusiasm for the kiwi hunt (also his continued collecting and export of kiwis abroad) contrasts sharply with his ardent support for the preservation of these and other bird species — another example of this contradiction in attitudes of scientists of the period.

Field observations were also made by Reischek (on *A. australis* and *A. owenii*), in which he noted aspects of their breeding behaviour, food and feeding, and habitat. Richard Henry kept specimens of *A. australis* in his garden at Lake Te Anau, and here, and later at Dusky Sound, he had ample opportunity to observe their behaviour and even to conduct experiments on feeding. His notes formed the basis of his book on the habits of New Zealand birds (which included some fanciful notions on the origins of the kiwis) as well as detailed reports made to the House of Representatives.

Study of the behaviour of captive kiwis continued in the twentieth century with papers by Haeusler (1923) and Robson (1947), while contributions from field study were made by Guthrie-Smith (1914) among others.

This, then, is the background to the discovery of the kiwis, their description by European naturalists, and the development of further study of these fascinating birds. Much was achieved in the nineteenth century, comparatively little during the first half of the twentieth. In spite of the application of new techniques and further effort on the part of biologists, the kiwis have still not given up all their secrets. More remains to be done, but what has been achieved recently will be looked at more closely in subsequent chapters of this book.

BIBLIOGRAPHY

Andrews, J. R. H. 1986. *The Southern Ark*. Century Hutchinson, Auckland.

Barclay, A. 1854. *Life of Captain Andrew Barclay* (as dictated to Thomas Scott). Privately published, Edinburgh.

Bartlett, A. D. 1852. On the genus Apteryx. *Proceedings of the Zoological Society of London*. 18: 274–6.

Beddard, F. E. 1899. See Rothschild.

Begg, A. C. and Begg, N. C. 1966. *Dusky Bay*. Whitcombe and Tombs, Christchurch.

Begg, A. C. and Begg, N. C. 1973. *Port Preservation*. Whitcombe and Tombs, Christchurch.

Bladen, F. M. 1901. *Historical Records of New South Wales*, v–vii, Bligh and Macquarie 1809, 1810, 1811. Government Printer, Sydney.

Buller, W. L. 1874. Notes on the Ornithology of New Zealand. *Transactions and Proceedings of the New Zealand Institute*, 6: 112–21.

Buller, W. L. 1876. On the Occurrence of *Apteryx oweni* at high altitudes in the North Island. *Transactions and Proceedings of the New Zealand Institute*. 8: 193–4.

Buller, W. L. 1877. (On the proposed Introduction of the Polecat into New Zealand). *Transactions and Proceedings of the New Zealand Institute*, 9: 634–5.

Buller, W. L. 1878. Further notes on the Ornithology of New Zealand. *Transactions and Proceedings of the New Zealand Institute*, 10: 201–9.

Buller, W. L. 1888. *A History of the Birds of New Zealand*. 2 v., 2nd ed. Published by the author, London.

Buller, W. L. 1891. (Exhibit of *Apteryx maxima*). *Transactions and Proceedings of the New Zealand Institute*, 23: 602–3.

Buller, W. L. 1892. Further Notes and Observations on Certain Species of New Zealand Birds (with Exhibits). *Transactions and Proceedings of the New Zealand Institute*, 24: 75–91.

Buller, W. L. 1892. On the large Kiwi from Stewart Island (*Apteryx maxima*.) *Transactions and Proceedings of the New Zealand Institute*, 24: 91–92.

Buller, W. L. 1893. Further notes on the Birds of New Zealand. *Transactions and Proceedings of the New Zealand Institute*, 25: 63–88.

Buller, W. L. 1895. Illustrations of Darwinism; or, The Avifauna of New Zealand considered in Relation to the Fundamental Law of Descent with Modification. *Transactions and Proceedings of the New Zealand Institute*, 27: 75–104.

Craigie, E. H. 1929. The cerebral cortex of *Apteryx*; evidence that the avian neocortex has been reduced from a multilaminar condition. *Anatomische Anzeiger*, Jena, 68(6/10): 97–105.
Craw, R. C. 1985. Classic problems of southern hemisphere biogeography re-examined. *Zeitschrift für zoologische Systematik und Evolutionsforschung*, 23: 1–10.
Cruise, R. A. 1823. *Journal of a Ten Months' Residence in New Zealand*. Longman, Hurst, Rees, Orme, and Brown, London.
Dumont d'Urville, J. S. C. 1853. *Voyage au Pôle Sud et dans l'Océanie sur les corvettes L'Astrolabe et la Zélée . . . pendant les années 1837–1838–1839–1840 etc. . . . Atlas, Zoologie*, Gide et Cie, Paris.
Durward, A. 1932. Observations on the cell masses in the cerebral hemisphere of the New Zealand Kiwi (*Apteryx australis*). *Journal of Anatomy*, 66: 437–77.
Farber, P. L. 1982. *The Emergence of Ornithology as a Scientific Discipline: 1760–1850*. D. Reidel, Dordecht.
Guthrie-Smith, W. H. 1914. *Mutton Birds and Other Birds*. Whitcombe and Tombs, Wellington.
Haeusler, H. R. 1923. Notes on the habits of the North Island Kiwi (*Apteryx mantelli*). *The Emu*. 22(3): 175–9.
Henry, R. 1896. On Dusky Sound. *Transactions and Proceedings of the New Zealand Institute*, 28: 50–54.
Henry, R. 1898. Notes on Bird-Life in the West Coast Sounds. *Transactions and Proceedings of the New Zealand Institute*, 30: 279–93.
Henry, R. 1903. Flightless Birds of New Zealand; and Other Notes. *New Zealand Parliament, House of Representatives, Appendices*. 1, c.–1: 126–30.
Henry, R. 1903. *The Habits of the Flightless Birds of New Zealand*. Government Printer, Wellington.
Hill, S. and Hill J. 1987. *Richard Henry of Resolution Island*. John McIndoe, Dunedin.
Hutton, F. W. 1873. On the Geographical Relations of the New Zealand Fauna. *Transactions and Proceedings of the New Zealand Institute*, 5: 227–56.
Hutton, F. W. 1893. On the origin of the Struthious birds of Australia. *Report of the Australasian Association for the Advancement of Science*, 4: 365–9.
Huxley, T. H. 1882. On the respiratory organs of *Apteryx*. *Proceedings of the Zoological Society of London*, 4: 560–9.
King, C. 1984. *Immigrant Killers*. Oxford University Press, Auckland.
King, M. 1981. *The Collector: A Biography of Andreas Reischek*. Hodder and Stoughton, Auckland.
Krabbe, K. H. 1957. Sur une formation singulière du cerveau d'un embryo de Kiwi (*Apteryx mantelli*). *Encéphale*, Paris, 5–6: 612–22.
Lankester, E. R. 1885. On the heart described by Professor Owen as that of *Apteryx*. *Proceedings of the Zoological Society of London*. 2: 239–40.
Lankester, E. R. 1885. On the Right Cardiac Valve of the Specimen of *Apteryx* dissected by Sir Richard Owen. *Proceedings of the Zoological Society of London*. 3: 477–82.
Lesson, R. P. 1828. *Manual d'Ornithologie ou Description des Genres et des Principales Espèces d'Oiseaux*. 2 v. Roret Libraire, Paris.
McNab, R. 1907. *Murihiku and the Southern Islands*, W. Smith, Invercargill.
Mivart, St. G. 1877. On the axial skeleton of the Struthionidae. *Transactions of the Zoological Society of London*, 10: 1–52.
Nicholas, J. L. 1817. *Narrative of a Voyage to New Zealand, Performed in the Years 1814 and 1815, in Company with the Rev. Samuel Marsden, Principal Chaplain of New South Wales*. 2 v. James Black and Sons, London.
Oliver, W. R. B. 1922. The birds of Little Barrier Island. *The Emu*, 22: 47.
Owen, R. 1839. (On the Anatomy of the Apteryx). *Proceedings of the Zoological Society of London*. 6: 48–51, 71, 72, 105–10.
Owen, R. 1840. On the anatomy of the Southern Apteryx (*Apteryx australis* Shaw). *Transactions of the Zoological Society of London*, 2: 257–302.
Parker, T. J. 1891. Observations on the anatomy and development of the *Apteryx*. *Philosophical Transactions of the Royal Society of London*, 183(B): 25–134.
Potts, T. H. 1870. On the Birds of New Zealand. *Transactions and Proceedings of the New Zealand Institute*, 2: 40–78.
Potts, T. H. 1872. Notes on a New Species of *Apteryx* (A. Haasti, Potts). *Transactions and Proceedings of the New Zealand Institute*, 4: 204–5.
Potts, T. H. 1873. On the Birds of New Zealand (Pt. III). *Transactions and Proceedings of the New Zealand Institute*, 5: 195.
Reischek, A. 1885. Notes on New Zealand Ornithology. *Transactions and Proceedings of the New Zealand Institute*, 17: 187–98.
Reischek, A. 1886. Observations on the Habits of New Zealand Birds, their Usefulness or Destructiveness to the Country. *Transactions and Proceedings of the New Zealand Institute*, 18: 96–104.
Richardson, J. (On the extinction of Native Birds on the West Coast). *New Zealand Journal of Science*, 1(5): 232–5.
Robson, F. D. 1947. *Kiwis in captivity: some observations on the famous flightless birds of New Zealand, as told to Robert Gibbings by F. D. Robson*. Hawke's Bay Art Gallery and Museum, Napier.
Rothschild, W. 1899. The Genus *Apteryx*. *Novitates Zoologicae*, 6: 361–402.
Shaw, G. and Nodder, F. P. 1789–1813. *The Naturalist's Miscellany*, 24 v. Published by the authors, London.
Turbott, E. G. 1967. *Buller's Birds of New Zealand*. Whitcoulls, Christchurch.
Whittell, H. M. 1947. Frederick Strange. *Australian Zoologist*, 11: 96–114.

The Species

2
BROWN KIWIS

BROWN KIWI

Apteryx australis Shaw and Nodder, 1813.

Apteryx australis Shaw and Nodder, 1813, *The Naturalist's Miscellany*, 24, pls. 1057, 1058.

DESCRIPTION

Head small; neck thick; body cone-shaped; tail not visible; wings rudimentary ending in a claw; feet and legs sturdy; bill long, slender and gently down-curved with tip of upper mandible projecting over lower and with nostrils at tip; base of bill surrounded with a hard cere and surrounded by whiskers; plumage shaggy and hair-like, each feather with weak barbs and no aftershaft; colour of plumage varies from blackish brown to greyish or rufous; feet and legs pale to dark brownish grey; bill horn-coloured or purplish grey (Stewart Island); iris black.

Sexes alike, although female is larger than male; young, similar to adults, only smaller.

MEASUREMENTS

Length: 500–650 mm.
Male: bill 110–155 mm; tarsus 58–85 mm; mid-toe 60–90 mm.
Female: bill 130–205 mm; tarsus 65–100 mm; mid-toe 70–95 mm.

EGGS

Clutch one to three; white or greenish white in colour (depending on subspecies); 115 × 70 mm to 137 × 83 mm.

RANGE

Forested areas of the North Island; Fiordland, south and central Westland; Stewart Island.

SUBSPECIES

Apteryx australis australis; Apteryx australis lawryi; Apteryx australis mantelli

On a handful of occasions, scientists have greeted the first published description of a newly discovered animal or bird with sheer disbelief. The most celebrated example is, perhaps, the platypus of Australia, a creature dismissed as a hoax by the nineteenth-century scholars who first examined the evidence for its existence. The first skins to arrive in England were scrutinised for signs of foul play (it was thought that they might have been concocted from skins and parts of several different animals), and only after considerable debate was it decided, reluctantly, to admit that such a wondrous animal might exist.

Shaw and Nodder's 1813 illustration of the brown kiwi received similar treatment — and it is easy to see why. The bird has such an unlikely combination of features that it seems better suited to a fairy story than to the real world. Its hair-like plumage, cat-like whiskers, prominent ear openings,

North Island brown kiwi, *Apteryx australis mantelli*. Oil, 1986.

absence of tail and visible wings, powerful legs and cone-shaped body are odd in themselves. But stranger still is the location of the nostrils, which, uniquely among birds, open near the tip of the long, slender bill; the kiwi's highly developed sense of smell is a most peculiar trait for a bird. Combine all this with nocturnal habits, reversal of sexual roles and the production of a huge egg, and kiwis can truly be thought of as a one-off evolutionary design; the scepticism that greeted their discovery is as understandable as the interest they have generated ever since.

Visitors to New Zealand must often think that New Zealanders are completely besotted by kiwis. And they are probably right; we refer to ourselves and to our dollars as kiwis, stamp kiwi symbols on our manufactured products, and watch cartoon kiwis on television. Kiwis are both the cornerstone of the national identity and our most familiar bird.

Yet, to a large degree, the interest is superficial. Many people are unaware that there are three species of kiwi, believing, instead, there to be just one. And for these people, the brown kiwi is *the* kiwi.

Perhaps this is as much a result of the brown kiwi's distribution as of anything else. The other two species, the little spotted and great spotted kiwis, have a much more restricted distribution and, in recent times at least, occur mostly in places not regularly frequented by humans. While the brown kiwi may also live in out-of-the-way places, it is present on all three of New Zealand's main islands — North, South and Stewart. It is also to be found on a number of smaller offshore islands, to which it has been introduced.

As might be expected with a bird occurring over such a large area, the species has been split into three subspecies: one for the South Island (*Apteryx australis australis*), one for Stewart Island (*Apteryx australis lawryi*) and one for the North Island (*Apteryx australis mantelli*). The physical differences that separate these subspecies are slight. The Stewart Island kiwi can be distinguished from the South Island brown by its larger size and purplish-grey beak; the North Island brown can be separated from both of the other two by its harsher, sharper plumage (this is particularly evident on the back of the neck and shoulders) and, usually, smaller size. Additional distinguishing features, such as colour or amount of whiskering, have been tentatively identified, but populations of kiwis can be variable, and most suggested differences have not proved constant.

Although these three subspecies are widely recognised and, from the geographical standpoint, quite convenient, there is evidence to suggest that their recognition may not be universal for very much longer. The early findings of a study of genetic profiles, led by Dr Charles Daugherty of Victoria University, suggest that changes are forthcoming, with some subspecies being combined and others created.

Despite being the most widespread of the kiwis, and despite its familiarity as an image, the brown kiwi is a surprisingly little-known bird from the scientific point of view. It is only in the last few years, with recent advances in night-viewing systems and radio-tracking equipment, that we have started to learn how kiwis live in the wild. Even though modern technology is providing the tools to overcome the problems presented by the birds' secretive and nocturnal behaviour, they are still difficult to study. Few people are willing to spend their nights pushing through heavy bush, following a bird that always seems to be just out of sight. In order to tag kiwis with a radio transmitter, the birds first have to be caught — and herein lies a big problem.

My own first attempts to radio-track brown kiwis in the Hawke's Bay area failed dismally. A large block of scrub containing about 30 kiwis was to be cleared for farming and it seemed realistic — particularly since there was a

Brown kiwi studies, *A. a. mantelli*. Pencil, 1982.

year in which to complete the work — to catch birds, release some in nearby reserves, and compare the survival of these with that of those remaining behind. For the first two months, I pushed my way through acres of scrub, hoping to stumble upon the bird at night — yet I didn't see a single one. On many occasions the birds called from only a few metres away, but the scrub that separated us was so thick that they might as well have been in the next valley.

With a fresh approach clearly required, I searched the early literature to learn how the Maoris had caught kiwis. Elsdon Best lists three methods: pitfall traps, trained dogs and lures — the birds being attracted with a combination of simulated calls and a smouldering piece of bark. According to Best, the glowing tip of rimu or koroi bark was revealed when a bird was nearby and the kiwi, perhaps thinking it had just sighted an enormous glow-worm, rushed in to grab it.

Whistling and taped calls had already been tried with no success, and I wasn't game to try wandering around the hills with smouldering bark under my shirt. Pitfall traps, however, seemed worth a try, and trained dogs clearly presented the best solution of them all. Unfortunately, the two years needed to train a pup into a competent kiwi dog were not available, but I did buy an oldish labrador of dubious breeding called Ben, who was supposedly already very accomplished at locating all types of game. At the same time, two pitfall traps were installed in an area where I had often found kiwi footprints.

For the next three months Ben and I combed the hills of the study area. Although Ben didn't find any kiwis (he was much too busy trying to rid himself of the muzzle he was made to wear), a young male kiwi was foolish enough to stumble into a pitfall trap — my first bird after five frustrating months.

More success followed. A friend with another labrador caught two kiwis in a fortnight, and Ben stunned everybody when he found a pair in a burrow. In all, six kiwis were caught in a year — too few to undertake the study planned. As it turned out, it didn't matter. The landowners changed their minds and designated the area a kiwi reserve.

There was little to show for the year other than a few snippets on the behaviour and ecology of the birds in the wild, but this is the nature of kiwi research — any information on the birds is extremely hard-won. I learned the importance of having a good dog, and so replaced Ben with a young bitch called Belle. For the next three years we worked together on the forests of Hawke's Bay, with occasional forays into Northland and Taranaki. During the same period two colleagues, Murray Potter and Michael Taborsky, began radio-tracking brown kiwis in the forests of Northland. A good deal of the information that follows results from our combined efforts.

VOCALISATION

Although few New Zealanders are lucky enough to see kiwis in the wild, many have heard their haunting calls, even if they haven't always been able to identify the bird making them. Brown kiwis make a variety of sounds, including grunts, growls, mews, purrs, squeals, clacks, chortles and whistles. The birds supposedly derive their name from the male's very loud, prolonged, shrill, ascending then descending whistle call — but this is better represented by *ah-eel* than *ki-wi*. Indeed, the first Maoris in New Zealand probably named the kiwi after a species found in their ancestral homeland — the kivi, or bristle-thighed curlew — which also has a long, slightly downcurved bill.

Head study of brown kiwi, *A. a. mantelli*. Oil, 1982.

Brown kiwi, *A. a. mantelli*, male. Oil, 1983.

Burrow of North Island brown kiwi — Hawke's Bay. Oil sketch, ND.

Kiwis begin calling as soon as they emerge from their daylight shelters, usually about three-quarters of an hour after sunset. The birds call throughout the night, but most often in the first two or three hours of darkness. The calls of females are much hoarser and more guttural than those of their mates. Their choking cry, which is somewhat akin to the heaving noises a cat makes just before it vomits, is instantly recognisable but not at all pleasant to listen to. Females start making this call at twelve to fourteen months.

Members of bonded pairs often reply to their mate's calls, and both birds sometimes duet or call together. Males call about three times more often than females, and their calls carry further — up to one and a half kilometres in still conditions. Both sexes call less often when it is windy, when there is a full moon, and when it is dry. The birds also vary their call rates throughout the year, with a peak in mid-winter (July) and a low in mid-summer (February).

Mews, purrs and grunts are soft sounds, made only when members of a pair are close together. All probably function as contact calls, though males sometimes purr while they copulate. Both sexes growl and clack their bill when handled, and probably also when they are approached by a predator. Chicks squeak when alarmed.

Studies of brown kiwis, *A. a. mantelli*, Oil, 1983.

Kiwis often exhale forcibly when feeding, apparently to clear dirt from their nostrils. This non-vocal noise is nevertheless fairly loud, and is audible

from about 15 metres. The birds also sniff loudly when approaching a strange object, seemingly testing the wind for clues to its identity, in much the same way as mammals do. Their highly developed, and most unusual, sense of smell provides their main means of locating food, especially on dark nights, when eyes are of little use.

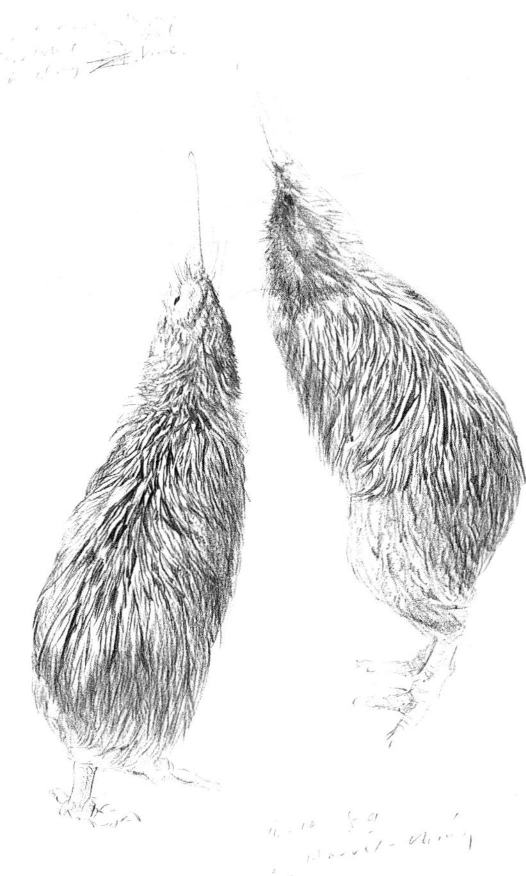

Brown kiwis, *A. a. mantelli*, reaching for earthworms in clay bank. Pencil, 1980.

DIET AND FEEDING BEHAVIOUR

Strong evolutionary forces are needed to make animals nocturnal. The sense of sight is so essential to survival that animals do not relinquish their dependence on it lightly. Kiwis probably became nocturnal either to avoid being eaten themselves, or to increase their own chances of finding food. The birds have shared parts of their long trek through evolutionary time with a variety of predators, most recently the mammals introduced by both Maoris and Europeans. However, before these mammals there were predatory birds, now known only from their subfossil remains. These included a large and formidable eagle, *Harpagornis*, and several smaller hunters such as crows, goshawks, and harrier hawks.

We can only guess at the impact these predators had on ground-dwelling birds, but it seems likely that much of the kiwi's behaviour today is a legacy of their past association with these hunters. The birds are cryptically coloured and, during daylight, continue to hide from predators that will never again appear in the skies overhead. The Stewart Island kiwi is not so strictly nocturnal as other kiwis and is perhaps just beginning to shake off the shackles of the past.

North and South Island brown kiwis emerge from daytime shelters when the first stars are beginning to show above the forest canopy. They enter a world already alive with other nocturnal animals: moths on the wing, wetas clicking on the branches, cockroaches and millipedes crawling over the litter, and the morepork (a small owl) hunting on silent wings. On still nights the air is heavy with the drone of beetles, fumbling their way through the darkness, and with the smell of damp leaf litter and humus. The forest is gripped in a quiet bustle as the nocturnal animals begin their shift.

The birds spend most of the night feeding, walking slowly among the undergrowth and ferns, sniffing quietly as they go. Soil invertebrates are their main quarry, which they capture by probing. The birds force their bill into the ground with a combination of vigorous body heaves and a back-and-forth levering motion of the head and neck. Sometimes they rotate at the same time, cork-screwing their bill downwards, usually until the short feathers on their faces press against the soil.

Probe holes are usually found in clusters, partly because of 'bad shots' and partly because the invertebrate prey are clumped. These holes are a sure sign of the presence of kiwi; no other animal in New Zealand makes smooth, large (up to 15 centimetres deep and 10 centimetres wide) cone-shaped holes in the forest floor.

Most food items are 10–20 millimetres long, and are extracted and eaten without difficulty. Sometimes, however, the birds tackle large prey such as the native worm, *Spenceriella gigantea*. These resemble a short (10–40 centimetres) length of garden hose, with a diameter to match. They are powerful and reluctant victims and usually escape after a brief struggle, about 90 per cent intact. But the battles are sometimes lengthy, and minutes can pass as the kiwi applies a steady strain and waits for the worm to yield. Some worms phosphoresce brightly as they are withdrawn from the soil, illuminating the kiwi's bill and face.

Brown kiwi, *A. a. mantelli*, feeding. Oil sketch, 1987.

Studies of foot and plumage of brown kiwi, *A. a. mantelli*. Pencil, 1983.

Brown kiwis in native forest, scrub and pine plantations mainly eat earthworms, cicada nymphs, scarabaeid larvae and various adult beetles. These are supplemented by spiders, fly larvae (chiefly tipulids), moth larvae, snails, centipedes, millipedes, crustaceans and small quantities of vegetable matter. Some seeds and berries are eaten for their food value; other large ones, such as hinau fruits, are consumed along with grit and stones to assist digestion. The birds seldom eat leaves in any quantity, but often swallow the odd one accidentally.

Kiwis living in rough farmland in Northland eat pasture pests such as white-fringed weevils, grass grubs and black field crickets, but too few to help farmers.

The birds are very much opportunists, taking whatever invertebrates are plentiful around them at the time. The manager of the nocturnal wildlife centre in Napier discovered this recently when he added a few frogs to a small pool in the kiwi enclosure to enhance the display. The kiwis are his star attraction, and their pen often has a throng of visitors around it. A few people were there when he released his new exhibits. About 20 minutes later he noticed an unusually large group around the kiwi pen, both fascinated and partly horrified by what they were witnessing. He hurried over to find the female kiwi struggling to swallow the fifth and last frog. Apparently, she had caught the first one in the water, and the others she had systematically tracked down, by scent, after they had fled from the pool.

A few weeks later, the manager tried adding two small eels to the pool. These, too, the female kiwi ate. She caught them by wading knee-deep through the pool, sweeping her bill from side to side, in much the same way as an avocet sweeps mud. She grabbed one eel in the middle, subdued it with a few vigorous thumps against the ground, and swallowed it more or less folded back on itself. The other was eaten end first, but it was hard to tell if it was the tail or head that led the way.

The remains of frogs and freshwater crayfish have been recovered from the droppings or gizzards of kiwis, so wild birds may also capture some foods in seepages and shallow waterways. The nasal valves of kiwis may exist specifically to enable the birds to feed in water.

In dry summers, kiwis feed mainly along the margins of swamps and in cool gullies, where the soil is still moist and penetrable. On wet nights the birds can be anywhere — on ridge tops, in gullies and on hillsides, including those with very steep slopes. The ranges of most kiwis contain a variety of landforms, perhaps reflecting the birds' seasonal needs for different kinds of feeding area.

DISPERSION AND SOCIAL BEHAVIOUR

Most brown kiwis live as bonded pairs in fixed territories throughout the year. Both sexes contribute to the defence of the territory. Their loud, whistling calls undoubtedly serve to advertise their presence, warning potential trespassers to keep clear. Intruders that do get caught are whistled at and chased off at high speed. Actual fights involving kicking are rare, but they have been seen between males and between females in pine forest at Waitangi. Such disputes are usually resolved before either protagonist is injured seriously, but they can be fatal when there is no opportunity for escape; this has happened from time to time in captivity, when birds have forced their way into their neighbours' pens.

Brown kiwis, *A. a. mantelli*, fighting. Pencil, 1989.

Mammals often use scent posts to mark their territories, and brown kiwis may do this too. Both the birds themselves and their faeces have a distinct,

A. mantelli
R. Harris-Ching
15-5-89

Brown kiwis, *A. a. mantelli*, fighting. Oil, 1987.

'My more intimate knowledge of the strange ways of the kiwi began at Kinpaka (North Auckland), when a neighbor's dog caught a young bird in the bush adjoining the settlement. It was unfortunately very badly hurt as a result of the dog's rough treatment, but as there seemed to be a possibility of saving its life, I decided to take it home and attend to its injuries.

'Already at this, our first meeting, the little fellow showed an unusually savage dispostion, for, although weak and evidently in great pain, it fought like a little demon, with legs and bill. I managed, however, to pick it up and carry it home but all my attempts to administer first aid failed. My young patient proved to be so unmanageable, and so vigorously resisted all attempts to treat its injured parts that I had to give up the idea of doing any amateur doctoring for the time. Hoping that it would become more tractable with better acquaintance and complete rest, and that freedom from worry would help it on the road to recovery, I placed the little kiwi in a yard fenced in with wire netting, and with a good-sized box for a house. Here it made itself quite at home, but it nevertheless rejected all my offers of friendship, and showed its vicious temper at every opportunity.

'In these decidedly unpleasant circumstances an event happened which promised to bring about a much more satisfactory state of things. Another kiwi appeared on the scene. It was a very old and remarkably quiet bird a dog had caught in the locality, which had been the home of the young bird. There was every reason, therefore, to expect that the newcomer would receive a most cordial welcome, but to my great surprise and disappointment this was not the case.

'No sooner did it notice the new arrival in the yard than the young bird made a furious rush at it and began to strike and pick at it in a most extraordinarily vicious manner, accompanying its blows with deep growls like those of an angry dog. The old bird, curiously enough, did not show the least sign of surprise or resentment. It took, in fact, absolutely no notice of its madly excited aggressor, although some of its kicks must be have been sufficiently hard to cause considerably pain, as I could judge from personal experience in a tussle with my young captive. Instead of doing so, and of teaching the youngster better manners, it calmly began to explore its new quarters, walking round and round, and carefully examining the wire netting with its bill.

'The two birds never became friends, the younger persisting in its hostile attitude, the other completely ignoring the other occupant of the yard. Only once did I notice the old bird knock the smaller one head over heels with a mighty kick.'

— H. R. Haeusler, RAOU, Notes on the Kiwi, *The Emu*, Vol. XXII, 1923

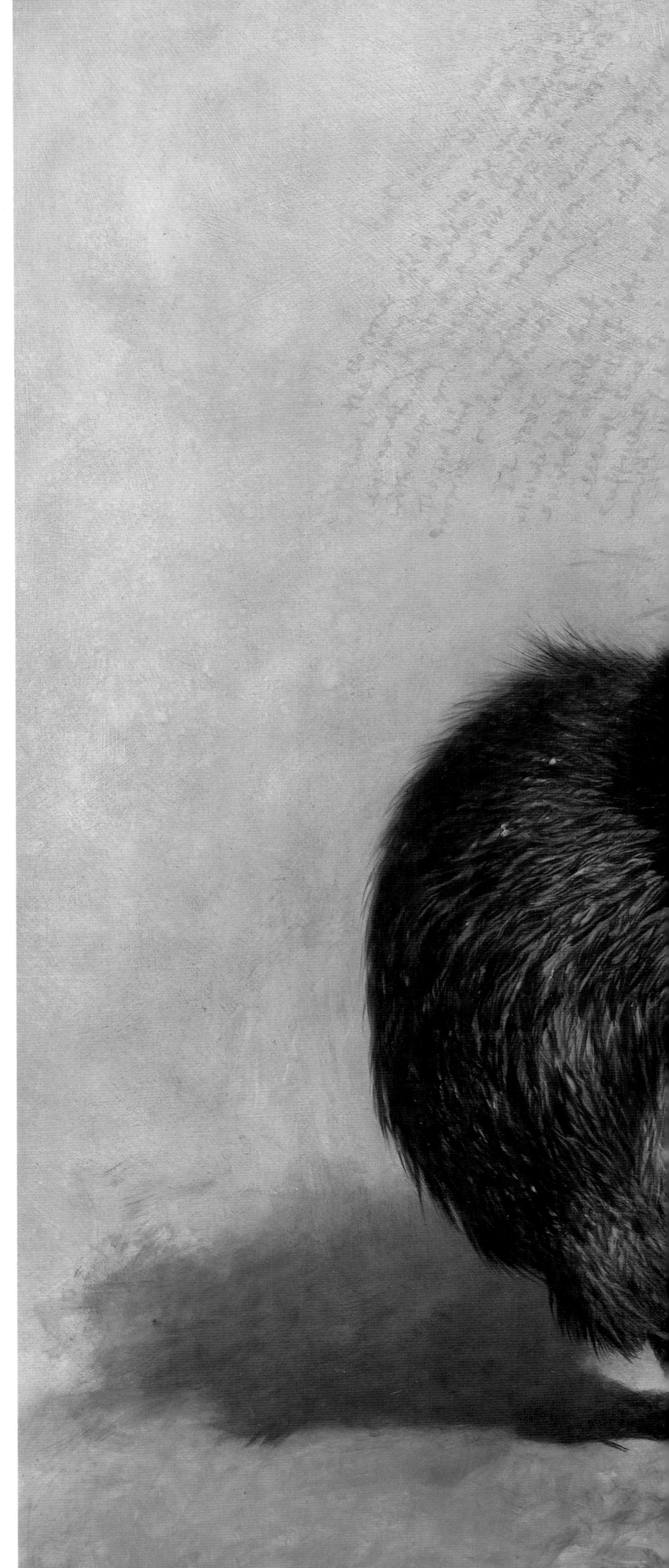

pungent smell that lingers in burrows for some days after the birds have used them. Kiwis intruding into occupied territories are quickly able to locate burrows that the residents have used. Lone females often add their faeces to any already in a burrow, perhaps to signal their availability to the resident (and already paired) male.

Territories may be costly to defend, but they provide the owners with the resources necessary for breeding and survival. Once established, kiwis usually remain within their territory for their entire life, even if it diminishes in quality. In the pine forests of Waitangi, for example, territories are often denuded when the trees are harvested. The occupants generally stay put and attempt to eke out an existence amongst the slash and debris left behind. They are reluctant to leave their territories for the unknown until forced out by the dwindling food supply in the cleared forest.

When I caught and radio-tagged my first brown kiwi, I returned the following day expecting to find the bird within a hundred metres or so of where I had released it. I switched on the receiver, waved the aerial about and listened for the blips from the bird's transmitter. There were none! I moved to the top of the nearest hill and tried again — with the same result. I eventually found my lost bird in the next valley, nearly a kilometre from where it had been caught. I had often heard a kiwi there before, but had always assumed that it was a different individual to the one that called on my side of the ridge. It just didn't seem possible that one bird would commute between two separate catchments.

I soon learned that brown kiwis (certainly those in Hawke's Bay) often travel a kilometre or more in a single night and have very large ranges, on average about 25 hectares. Furthermore, these large ranges were in fact territories, occupied by members of a pair or by a single adult who prevented other kiwis from using them. It seems extraordinary that a flightless, hen-sized bird can defend a patch of forest equivalent in size to about sixty football fields. I had initially thought, from counting calls, that my study area contained about 70 kiwis; radio-tracking revealed the true number to be about 30. We now know that most forests in Hawke's Bay contain fewer than two pairs of kiwis per hundred hectares.

Most territories were more or less rectangular in shape, except for one occupied by a female bird. Her range was a narrow, circular strip, around the territories of three pairs; it looked like a road when plotted on a map. The circuit, nearly five and a half kilometres long, weaved through three valley systems and took its owner about five nights to walk round.

These observations, obtained by radio-tracking in the Hawke's Bay area, are similar to observations made by Murray Potter in Northland. In a 200-hectare reserve, estimated to contain a very dense population of about a hundred kiwis, Potter found the birds to have ranges of about thirty hectares. There was, however, much overlap between neighbours; some parts of the reserve were used by as many as twelve different kiwis. The birds were territorial only in the breeding season, and their ranges then contracted to about five hectares.

BREEDING

Female brown kiwis are up to 25 per cent larger and heavier than males. This difference between the sexes is evident in all subspecies, although the northern birds may be smaller overall than those in the south. The North Island birds are lightest in mid-summer (January) and heaviest in mid-winter (July), just before they begin laying. Females at peak weight tip the scales at nearly four

Studies of chicks of brown kiwi, *A. a. mantelli*. Oil on two panels, 1981.

1 DAY OLD

kilograms, about a kilogram more than males, and sometimes give their mate a solid kick if they are not feeling receptive to his advances.

Members of bonded pairs spend most of their time together in the week or two before the first egg is laid. They usually shelter together during the day, often in a hole within 50 metres of where they will eventually lay. They seldom visit the nest site itself, other than to line the chamber with a thin layer of leaves and grasses. The birds nest mainly in short burrows (about 65 centimetres long) dug into the side of steep banks, but occasionally use hollow logs, fissures in rocks, and hollows under thick vegetation. Nesting burrows are excavated months and perhaps years before they are used, long enough for moss and small ferns to re-establish at the burrow entrance and for all traces of excavated soil to disappear. The birds seem to take great care to ensure that the nest blends with its surroundings, but, strangely, the burrow itself is often located in an open area with little vegetation nearby.

The female stops eating for one or two days before she lays. At this stage the egg almost entirely fills her body cavity and distends her belly; there is no room for food as well. She walks with legs a little wider apart than usual, and can manage an awkward rolling run. Sometimes at night she stands belly deep in water, perhaps to cool down or take the weight off her feet.

The egg, when it comes, is laid quickly and with little effort. It is white to greenish white, oval, and about 130 millimetres in length and 78 in width. It weighs about 430 grams, some 14–20 per cent of the female's pre-laying weight, and is more than four times larger than might theoretically be expected from a kiwi-sized bird.

The egg's astonishing size is just one of its marvels. Underneath the thin shell is a large, greyish-yellow yolk that comprises about 60 per cent of the contents. The yolk, relative to the size of egg, is 50 to 100 per cent larger than those of other birds. This makes kiwi eggs the richest of any known, equivalent in energy to about a dozen hen's eggs. (This fact was fully appreciated by the early Maoris, who prized the eggs for their food value and ate them on ceremonial occasions.) The shell itself has fewer pores than might be expected, to preserve water during the long incubation period, and the albumen is rich in natural bacteriacides and fungicides to thwart any microbes that might sneak in through the pores.

The female remains in the nest for a day after laying. Thereafter, the egg is incubated entirely by the male. He often makes a faltering start, incubating intermittently for a week or two before settling into a steady routine. The female, in the meantime, feeds steadily. It takes her about 25 to 30 days to make her second egg, and she supplies about half the materials for it from her own stored reserves. She loses about 180–200 grams of body weight each time she lays. She completes the clutch with her second egg, although on rare occasions she might add a third after another thirty days. If the first clutch fails early in incubation, the birds move to a new nest and the female re-lays another two eggs. These, too, will be replaced if they fail, so some females lay five or six eggs in as many months. This is why females do not help with incubation; they have to feed throughout the night to meet the huge energetic costs of egg production.

By the time the second egg arrives, the male has developed a large, vasculated brood patch on his lower belly, and is spending about 20 hours of each day incubating. He emerges to feed and defecate every night, carefully covering the burrow entrance with vegetation before he moves away. He remains off the nest for an average of four or five hours, long enough for the eggs to cool down to ambient temperature. Occasionally he takes a whole night off, and sometimes the next day as well, returning to the eggs after an

Day-old chick, brown kiwi, *A. a. mantelli*. Pencil, 1987.

absence of some 20 hours. The eggs, which are usually buried to the midline in vegetation, are unharmed by these long periods of chilling. By the end of incubation the male is quite skinny, having metabolised about 35 grams of fat (18 per cent of his pre-incubation weight) to make up for his restricted foraging.

All being well, the first egg hatches after 75 to 84 days of incubation, followed by the second egg some five to thirteen days later. Hatching takes two or three days; chicks lack an egg tooth, and use their feet to break through the shell. The chicks emerge wet, slimy, unable to stand, and with their belly distended with nearly half of the egg's original store of yolk. This nourishes them for their first week of life. After three days they have dried off and can shuffle around the nest. The male broods them during the day and for about half of the night, aided occasionally by the female. Neither parent feeds the chicks. When they are five or six days old, the chicks emerge for the first time to probe within a few metres of the nest. Their forays increase in duration and distance as they get older and bolder; by ten days they are away for most of the night. They continue to return to the nest during the day for another week, then finally leave it for good when about 20 days old. At this stage they are a perfect kiwi in miniature, a 300-gram powder-puff of feathers on the forest floor.

We know little about what they do in the next few years. In the North Island subspecies, chicks probably wander until they reach sexual maturity some eighteen months (male) to three years (female) later. In the southern subspecies, chicks may remain within their natal territories for some months, maintaining a loose bond with their parents.

BREEDING SUCCESS

Most kiwi eggs never in fact hatch. Some are accidentally cracked or chipped by the incubating male, some are invaded by microbes, a few are eaten by predators, some are infertile, and some disappear without trace. Hatching success in both Hawke's Bay and Northland is about 25 per cent. It may be lower still in the southern subspecies, which overlaps in range with wekas (*Gallirallus australis*), the only native predator of kiwi eggs. These endemic, flightless rails sometimes raid nests when incubating males are away foraging. The kiwi's habit of concealing its nest with vegetation has probably evolved as a defence to predation by wekas; the two species have coexisted for at least 25 million years.

Some chicks die while hatching and others die before they reach independence. Chicks are particularly clumsy and accident-prone when they first emerge from the nest. In Hawke's Bay, two six-day-old chicks died after becoming entangled in cleft sticks. Ironically, in one instance, the stick had been placed at the entrance of the nest by the incubating male. Having watched that particular chick on the previous two nights, I was both annoyed and saddened that it should get into trouble when there was no help to hand.

In Hawke's Bay, only about half of the chicks that hatch survive until they are old enough to leave the nest. Pairs fledge, on average, one chick every two years. Murray Potter recorded a similar rate of production in Northland. Brown kiwis are long-lived (up to 35 years in captivity), so probably only about one chick in seven needs to survive to adulthood to replace each adult pair. We know nothing about their journey from independence to adulthood, but it is undoubtedly a hazardous one. Chicks are too small and slow to defend themselves against cats, ferrets or stoats. Furthermore, these mammals are also active at night, so chicks gain no protection from them by being

Chestnut variety of brown kiwi, *A. a. mantelli*. Oil, 1985.

Apteryx australis
mantelli

nocturnal. Few chicks probably reach adulthood; it may be considered astonishing that some do.

CONCLUDING COMMENTS

The brown kiwi's story is one of extraordinary survival, at times against incredible odds. The ancestor of the kiwis which also spawned the moa lineage, first walked on mainland New Zealand some 70 million years ago. Through the millenia they have endured climate changes, glaciations, and successive retreats and expansions of forest. And in the last thousand years, they have survived perhaps the severest of all challenges — the arrival of humans.

It might be thought that they should have been one of the first to yield to human presence. Long-lived, flightless, slow-reproducing, ground-nesting birds are easy prey and slow to recover from the depredations of hunters. All the species of moa eventually succumbed to the spears, dogs and fires of the early Maoris, but the kiwis didn't.

The pace of land clearance accelerated when the Europeans arrived, especially in the North Island. The forests were beaten back, valley by valley, towards high ground. The new colonists also introduced a whole new range of mammals, birds and avian diseases, often fully aware of their probable impacts on New Zealand's native animals. But they were concerned only with re-creating the homeland they had left behind; there was no collective desire to preserve the special flavour of their new surroundings.

Several species of native bird perished during the late 1800s, and others disappeared from large parts of the country; more have vanished during this century. But the brown kiwi survived. It is astonishing that these birds withstood the packs of wild dogs that roamed through the forests at one time. One wild dog can devastate a kiwi population in a matter of months, as happened recently in Waitangi forest in Northland.

The Europeans, like the Maoris before them, hunted kiwis for their feathers. Thousands were killed and sent to Europe to satisfy the demands of Victorian fashion. It was big money for the collectors of the day. Large skins from females were worth £3 7s 6d in 1870. But the kiwis survived this onslaught too.

Today, all kiwis are fully protected by law; perhaps even more significantly, their habitats are not. The North Island subspecies is still retreating, forest by forest, as land continues to be cleared for farming and exotic plantations. Each year, hundreds of kiwis are maimed or killed in gin traps set for the introduced possum; others are killed by a variety of predators, including the dogs used to hunt feral pigs. The birds are still under siege — and will remain so — until they finally submit. And sooner or later they will do that, unless they are given a helping hand.

For most New Zealanders, the kiwi symbolises the uniqueness of the land and people. For me, the birds exemplify the curious workings of evolution and the strange paths that it sometimes follows. In addition, they symbolise tenacity — probably a desirable quality for a national emblem.

BIBLIOGRAPHY

Bartlett, L. 1850. *Apteryx mantelli*, the North Island brown kiwi. *Proceedings of the Zoological Society*, 275.

Best, E. 1942. *Forest Lore of the Maori.* Government Printer, Wellington.

Bull, P. C., Gaze, P. D. and Robertson, C. J. R. 1985. *The Atlas of Bird Distribution in New Zealand.* The Ornithological Society of New Zealand, Wellington.

BROWN KIWIS

Buller, W. L. 1888. *A History of the Birds of New Zealand*, vol. 2, 2nd edn. The author, London.

Buller, W. L. 1896. Notes on the ornithology of New Zealand. *Transactions and Proceedings of the New Zealand Institute*, 29: 179–207.

Calder, W. A. 1979. The kiwi and egg design: evolution as a package deal. *Bioscience*, 29: 461–7.

Colbourne, R. and Powlesland, R. G. 1988. Diet of the Stewart Island brown kiwi (*Apteryx australis lawryi*) at Scolley's Flat, southern Stewart Island. *New Zealand Journal of Ecology*, 11: 99–104.

Fleming, C. A. 1962. History of the New Zealand landbird fauna. *Notornis*, 9: 270–4. censusing populations. *Notornis*, 31: 191–201.

Colbourne, R. and Powlesland, R. G. 1988. Diet of the Stewart Island Brown Kiwi (*Apteryx australis lawryi*) at Scolley's Flat, southern Stewart Island. *New Zealand Journal of Ecology*, 11: 99–104.

Fleming, C. A. 1962. History of the New Zealand landbird fauna. *Notornis,*, 9: 270–4.

Goudswaard, R. 1985. Breeding of the North Island brown kiwi (*Apteryx australis mantelli*) at the Wellington Zoo. *Thylacinus*, 10: 9–19.

Gould, S. J. 1986. Of kiwi eggs and the Liberty Bell. *Natural History*, 11: 20–29.

Guthrie-Smith, H. 1914. *Mutton Birds and Other Birds*. Whitcombe and Tombs, Christchurch.

Haeusler, H. R. 1923. Notes on the habits of the North Island Kiwi. *Emu*, 22: 175–9.

Hill, S. and Hill, J. 1987. *Richard Henry of Resolution Island*. John McIndoe Ltd, Dunedin. 364 pp.

Jolly, J. 1985. Little spotted kiwi: paradise regained or paradise lost? *Forest & Bird*, 16: 15–17.

Kleinpaste, R. and Colbourne, R. 1983. Kiwi food study. *New Zealand Journal of Ecology*, 6: 143–4.

McLennan, J. A., Rudge, M. R. and Potter, M. A. 1987. Range size and denning behaviour of brown kiwi, *Apteryx australis mantelli*, in Hawke's Bay, New Zealand. *New Zealand Journal of Ecology*, 10: 97–107.

McLennan, J. A. 1988. Breeding of North Island brown kiwi, *Apteryx australis mantelli*, in Hawke's Bay, New Zealand. *New Zealand Journal of Ecology*, 11: 89–97.

Oliver, W. R. B. 1955. *New Zealand Birds*. A. H. & A. W. Reed, Wellington.

Rasch, G. and Kayes, P. 1985. The second survey of the brown kiwi in Waitangi State Forest. New Zealand Forest Service, unpublished report.

Reid, B. 1971. Composition of a kiwi egg. *Notornis*, 18: 250–2.

Reid, B. and Williams, G. R. 1975. The kiwi. In: *Biogeography and Ecology in New Zealand*. Kuschel, G. (editor). Junk, The Hague, pp. 301–30.

Reid, B. and Rowe, B. 1978. Management of kiwis in captivity. *Otorohanga Zoological Society Progress Report*, Otorohanga.

Reid, B., Ordish, R. G. and Harrison, M. 1982. An analysis of the gizzard contents of 50 North Island brown kiwis, *Apteryx australis mantelli*, and notes on feeding observations. *New Zealand Journal of Ecology*, 5: 76–85.

Reid, B. 1981. Size discrepancy between eggs of wild and captive brown kiwi. *Notornis*, 28: 281–7.

Robson, F. D. 1947. Kiwis in captivity. *Bulletin of the Hawke's Bay Museum*, Napier.

Rothschild, W. L. 1893. Notes on the genus *Apteryx*. *Bulletin of the British Ornithologists' Club*, 1: 59–61.

Shaw, G. and Nodder, F. P. 1813. *Naturalists' Miscellany* 24, plate 1057.

Taborsky, M. 1988. Kiwis and dog predation: observations in Waitangi State Forest. *Notornis*, 35: 197–202.

Watt, J. C. 1971. The North Island kiwi: a predator of pasture insects. *New Zealand Entomologist*, 5: 25–27.

Wenzel, B. M. 1968. Olfactory prowess in the kiwi. *Nature*, 220: 1133–4.

3

THE SOUTH ISLAND BROWN KIWI

SOUTH ISLAND BROWN KIWI

Apteryx australis australis Shaw and Nodder, 1813.

Apteryx australis Shaw and Nodder, 1813, *The Naturalist's Miscellany*, 24, pls. 1057, 1058.
Apteryx fusca Potts, 1873, *Transactions of the New Zealand Institute*, 5, p. 196.

DISTINGUISHING FEATURES

Usually larger and lighter in colour than *mantelli* yet smaller than *lawryi*; the feathers are less hard and less stiff to the touch than those of *mantelli*.

MEASUREMENTS

Length: 500–600 mm.
Male: bill 110–125 mm; tarsus 60–80 mm; mid-toe 80–90 mm.
Female: bill 150–170 mm; tarsus 70–80 mm; mid-toe 85–95 mm.

EGGS

Clutch one to two; colour white; 120 × 74 mm to 127 × 82 mm.

RANGE

Fiordland; south Westland.

During the month of May in the year 1812, a kiwi skin arrived — from New Zealand via Sydney — in England. Its exact place of origin is unknown, but for many, many years it has been considered probable that the bird was obtained at Dusky Sound, close to the south-west tip of the South Island. Perhaps rather surprisingly, the skin still exists; it can be seen today at the Liverpool Museum, where it survives in remarkably good condition. Taking no chances with posterity, however, Shaw and Nodder had, by the end of 1813, described the bird in their *Naturalist's Miscellany* and bestowed upon it the scientific name *Apteryx australis* — the southern wingless bird.

For some years this specimen remained unique in Europe, but, as time passed, more and more brown kiwis — from all parts of New Zealand — became available for study. It became apparent that certain differences, albeit slight ones, existed between the specimens coming from the South Island and those brought from the North.

Birds with a South Island provenance were generally found to be larger and somewhat lighter in colour than their North Island counterparts, but the most constant factor separating the two forms was the softer nature of the plumage of South Island birds. In North Island individuals, the shafts of the

South Island brown kiwi, *Apteryx australis australis*. Oil, 1986.

feathers project well beyond the barbs, giving a harsher, spiky appearance, this being particularly noticeable about the area of the neck and shoulder.

The South Island brown kiwi lives almost entirely in remote, uninhabited areas. Its stronghold is in Fiordland, in the peaks and hanging glacial valleys between the Hollyford and Waitutu Rivers. Here the birds inhabit a steep and dramatic landscape, perhaps the harshest of any in New Zealand. They are to be found from sea level to the areas of tussock above the timberline; presumably they venture into the treeless places at night, returning to their holes in the forest by day.

A second, smaller population lives in South Westland, on the flanks of the Southern Alps, between the Haast and Arawata Rivers. It may still be linked to the Fiordland population, although recent surveys suggest that there are now few kiwis in the forests between the Hollyford and Arawata.

South Island brown kiwi, *A. australis*, studies at the Fox Glacier. Oil on prepared panel, 1983.

Typical habitat of the South Island brown kiwi, *A. australis*.
Photo: Jaan Voot

plate 5
adult birds below
Fox Glacier

Raised feathers in
display of aggression
by S.I. Brown kiwi
August 15th.
1982.

SOUTH ISLAND BROWN KIWI

The third, and smallest, population of South Island brown kiwis is in the coastal forests surrounding Okarito Lagoon. These birds are definitely isolated from those further south and may have always been. Their appearance and genetic profiles indicate that their ancestors came from the north rather than the south. Colonisation from the north was possible during the Pleistocene glaciation, when the North and South Islands were connected. But perhaps a more probable explanation for these seemingly misplaced birds is that Maoris, who sometimes carried kiwis in their canoes, liberated them near the lagoon during the last century.

The Okarito area has an additional significance in that it is close to the home of the great spotted kiwi. Nowhere else do the two species live in such close proximity. The area is potentially of great value for comparative studies of both the habitat requirements of the two species and the factors that led to their separate development.

While none of the kiwis are well known, the South Island subspecies of the brown kiwi is probably the least known of all; certainly most brown kiwi research has been centred around North Island birds. Presumably, this is chiefly due to the remoteness of the South Island brown's home grounds, where all the factors that inhibit kiwi research generally are so much accentuated. Very little recent study has been undertaken, but the very inaccessibility of this subspecies will, perhaps, render its future at least as secure as that of any of its relatives.

South Island brown kiwi, *A. australis*, with feathers raised in threat. Pencil, 1982.

4

THE STEWART ISLAND BROWN KIWI

STEWART ISLAND BROWN KIWI

Apteryx australis lawryi Rothschild, 1893.

Apteryx lawryi Rothschild, 1893, *Ibis*, p. 575

DISTINGUISHING FEATURES

Closer to *australis* than *mantelli*; usually larger than both (considerably bigger than *mantelli*) and often with a more rufous hue to the plumage than *australis*; bill purplish grey (rather than horn-coloured); legs and feet slate grey.

MEASUREMENTS

Length: 600–650 mm
Male: bill 130–155 mm; tarsus 70–85 mm; mid-toe 80–90 mm
Female: bill 160–205 mm; tarsus 75–100 mm; mid-toe 85–95 mm

EGGS

Clutch two; colour greenish white; 130 × 79 mm to 137 × 83 mm.

RANGE

Stewart Island; Ulva Island.

Stewart Island lies some 40 kilometres across the Foveaux Strait south from Bluff. It is the biggest of New Zealand's offshore islands and figured quite largely in the early history of New Zealand's colonisation, when it was favoured by sealers and whalers. At one time it was, in fact, important enough to be known as the South Island, with today's South Island being generally referred to as the 'Middle Island'.

It is, perhaps, hardly surprising that a population of flightless birds living in island isolation should develop certain features and habits distinguishing them from others of their kind, and this seems to be the case with the Stewart Island kiwi.

Differences in appearance between the kiwis of Stewart Island and those living on the South Island were first noticed by Walter Lawry Buller, who exhibited a skin before a meeting of the Wellington Philosophical Society in 1890. For technical reasons, the scientific name that Buller proposed for this new form was declared invalid, but in 1893 Walter Rothschild, English naturalist and author, put forward another name — and one that commemorated Buller himself — for the Stewart Island kiwi: *Apteryx lawryi*.

The distinguishing feature of this kiwi is the size of its bill and leg, which are substantially larger than those of its relatives on the other side of Foveaux

Stewart Island brown kiwi, *Apteryx australis lawyri*, studies of male (above), female (below) and burrow entrance in flax. Oil (detail), 1989.

Habitat of *A. a. lawyri* at Masons Bay, Stewart Island.
Photo: Jaan Voot

Strait. In a rare display of harmony, the scientific community accepted the species without reservation, although the 'species' was later relegated to the status of subspecies: *Apteryx australis lawryi*.

Not only the bird's great size separates it from its South Island relatives; it shows other unique features. The bill is quite different in colour. Whereas both North and South Island brown kiwis have horn-coloured beaks, those of Stewart Island birds are slate grey with a purplish hue; their feet and legs are blue grey. The eggs are also distinct, being greenish white rather than just white.

The habits of Stewart Island kiwis are unusual in several respects. The birds sometimes emerge in daylight, and at night they are often to be seen on beaches, probing along the strandline. The sandhills there are criss-crossed with the tracks of both kiwis and penguins — a combination seldom encountered elsewhere in New Zealand. Another peculiarity is that Stewart Island kiwis occupy overlapping home ranges. The population appears to have increased greatly in recent years, and the birds in most parts are now so numerous that it is probably impossible for pairs or individuals to defend feeding areas. Parts of the island appear to be common ground, available to any bird that happens by. One such patch (a ten-hectare clump of kanuka) near Masons Bay was used by 23 different kiwis in the course of just a few nights. Stewart Island is the only place known where kiwis sometimes feed and roost in small, mixed-age groups. These may well be families — an adult pair with their offspring from the previous one or two breeding seasons — but studies are needed to confirm this.

This southernmost subspecies is found throughout Stewart Island and on one small islet (Ulva) off its eastern coast. Stewart Island kiwis are the easiest of all the kiwis to observe in the wild and have become something of an attraction for New Zealanders and overseas visitors. The island itself may be fairly remote, but for many people the effort of getting there is richly rewarded by the sight of one of these strange birds snuffling through the undergrowth or wandering across the sand.

Studies of *A. a. lawyri*, in the tussock grass on Stewart Island. Pencil, 1987.

5

THE NORTH ISLAND BROWN KIWI

NORTH ISLAND BROWN KIWI

Apteryx australis mantelli Bartlett, 1850.

Apteryx mantelli Bartlett, 1850, *Proceedings of the Zoological Society of London*, p. 275.
Apteryx bulleri Sharpe, 1888, *Proceedings of the Wellington Philosophical Society*, p. 6.

DISTINGUISHING FEATURES

Usually smaller than *australis* (considerably smaller than *lawryi*) and often darker in colour; shafts of feathers project well beyond the barbs giving a more wiry, spiky appearance when seen close to, particularly evident around the neck and shoulder.

MEASUREMENTS

Length: 500–550 mm.
Male: bill 110–140 mm; tarsus 58–70 mm; mid-toe 60–75 mm.
Female: bill 130–180 mm; tarsus 65–90 mm; mid-toe 70–85 mm.

EGGS

Clutch one to three; colour white; 115 × 70 mm to 135 × 80 mm.

RANGE

Forested areas of the North Island north of the Manawatu Gorge; Little Barrier Island.

In the early days of New Zealand ornithology, with naturalists competing intensely against each other to discover and describe new species, the most minute differences between specimens were sometimes used to justify a new name or designation. Brown kiwis were subjected to the same scrupulous inspections as other kinds of birds, and eventually the small differences that separate North and South Island brown kiwis were spotted.

A. D. Bartlett, superintendent of the Zoological Gardens of London, was the first naturalist to notice distinguishing features, and in 1850 he claimed that the North Island brown kiwi was a separate species, *Apteryx mantelli*, on the grounds that it was slightly smaller, darker in colour and had harsher plumage than its southern counterpart.

The validity of this distinction was debated fiercely during the next two decades. Buller and Potts supported Bartlett; other notables of the day, such as Finsch, Sclater, Rowley and Sharpe, did not. No fewer than fourteen publications were devoted exclusively to this subject — with neither side being able to convince the other. Even more controversial was a move to split the North Island brown kiwi itself into two species on the basis of plumage colour. The move created *Apteryx bulleri*, but its appearance in the literature

Female North Island brown kiwi, *Apteryx australis mantelli*, and chick.
Watercolour, 1980

was short-lived, even Buller's most devoted followers being unable to rally behind it.

Today, the North Island brown kiwi is no longer regarded as a species in its own right, but its distinguishing features are thought sufficient to merit subspecific status: *Apteryx australis mantelli*.

The most reliable point of separation between this subspecies and the other two (*australis* and *lawryi*) is the harsher, more spiky appearance of the plumage of North Island birds. Other features, such as darker colouration and smaller size, may be correctly observed, but these are not necessarily constant factors, there being a considerable degree of individual variation and, therefore, overlap in these qualities.

Apteryx australis mantelli still survives in most large tracts of forest north of latitude 40°S. The birds are particularly plentiful in Northland and in rough hill country in inland Taranaki and Wanganui. A third, smaller population is centred on the Bay of Plenty and East Coast, extending south to Napier.

Typical North Island subtropical rainforest habitat of *A. a. mantelli*.
Photo: Jaan Voot

Partial albino North Island brown kiwi, *A. a. mantelli*, at Otorohanga. Oil sketch, ND.

These kiwis occupy a diverse range of habitats — rough farmland, regenerating scrub, pine plantations and dense rainforest — often in close proximity to humans.

A particularly large population, estimated at about a thousand birds, lives in a pine plantation at Waitangi, just a few kilometres north of one of New Zealand's main tourist centres at Kerikeri in the Bay of Islands. Elsewhere in Northland, and in inland Taranaki, local residents often hear the birds calling at night, and sometimes see them wandering through gardens.

Some kiwis turn up in the most unlikely places. A few years ago, a juvenile was found feeding amongst a flock of sheep in hills near Napier, some kilometres away from the nearest patch of bush. More recently, a kiwi was found in a hen house at Coromandel, much to the surprise of the owner (and probably the hens).

The North Island brown kiwi is the most often encountered and best known of New Zealand's kiwis, simply because it lives so close to humans.

GREAT SPOTTED KIWI
Marlborough.
South Island.

6

THE GREAT SPOTTED KIWI

GREAT SPOTTED KIWI

Apteryx haastii Potts, 1871.

Apteryx haastii Potts, 1871, *Transactions of the New Zealand Institute*, 6, p. 204.

DESCRIPTION

Head small; neck thick; body cone-shaped; tail not visible; wings rudimentary; feet and legs sturdy; bill long, slender and gently down-curved with tip of upper mandible projecting over lower and with nostrils at tip; base of bill surrounded by whiskers; plumage shaggy and hair-like, each feather with a single shaft and unlinked barbs; upper parts of head and neck charcoal grey; throat and belly pale grey; rest of plumage predominantly grey mottled and banded with blackish brown but showing a varying degree of chestnut on the back; feet and legs usually dark brown but sometimes creamy white; claws black in young birds, horn-coloured in older ones; bill pale ivory suffused with pink, sometimes with a slate grey line on upper mandible; iris black.

Sexes alike, although female is larger than male; young, similar to adults, only smaller.

DISTINGUISHING FEATURES

Mottled appearance distinguishes this species from *Apteryx australis*; large size and chestnut hue to the plumage of the back separate it from *A. owenii*.

MEASUREMENTS

Length: 500–600 mm
Male: bill 90–100 mm; tarsus 80–105 mm; mid-toe 85–90 mm.
Female: bill 125–135 mm; tarsus 85–110 mm; mid-toe 90–95 mm.

EGGS

Clutch one; colour pale greenish white; 120 × 69 mm to 130 × 85 mm.

RANGE

South Island, mainly west of Main Divide from Tasman Bay to south Westland.

The mid-1800s was an exciting time for New Zealand ornithology. New species were being described regularly, and rumours abounded of yet more unnamed birds, often said to be more spectacular than those already discovered.

One such animal was a very large kiwi that was believed to live in the rugged ranges of the west coast of the South Island of New Zealand. The local Maoris referred to it as roaroa (roa means long or tall) or kiwi-karuai, the kiwi with the watery eyes. They claimed it was at least twice the size of the brown kiwi, a view that was echoed by some of the early European explorers. Mr Rochfort, for example, the provincial surveyor of Nelson in the 1850s, described the roaroa as 'about the size of a turkey — very powerful, having spurs on his legs — which, when attacked by a dog, defends himself so well as

Great spotted kiwi, *Apteryx haastii*, and chick. Oil, 1985.

frequently to come off victorious'. Its calls, according to the explorer Dr Julius von Haast, were so much louder than those of the brown kiwi that it was like comparing 'the voice of a powerful man to the cry of a child'.

Despite these tantalising descriptions and claims of first-hand experience, actual specimens of the roaroa proved to be elusive. Not a single skin or feather of the giant kiwi had found its way into a museum. This, however, did not seem to bother Jules Verreaux, an ornithologist travelling with the ship *Astrolabe*. He decided that the species definitely existed and, with nothing else but commendable confidence, gave it the grand and appropriate name of *Apteryx maxima*.

For the next two decades or so, the species was hunted by bird collectors, each eager to procure the first specimen. A steady trickle of reports of giant kiwis from Martins Bay and other parts of Westland undoubtedly sharpened their resolve, but did nothing to improve their success. Frederick Hutton thought he might have struck the jackpot after examining the tarsus and foot of a kiwi caught by gold-diggers in 1868 in the upper Aorere River in north-west Nelson. The diggers had eaten the bird, but had been so impressed with its size that they had weighed it when fresh and kept one of the legs. They claimed it was nearly 14 pounds (6.4 kilograms)! Sadly, however, Hutton's measurements of the tarsus (3 inches long) and middle toe (3¼ inches to the tip of the claw) suggested a kiwi of near-normal size. The diggers themselves, swept up in the excitement of the 'Bergoo' rush, were perhaps thinking more of the gold they were going to find than of the kiwi itself when they weighed the bird.

Many rumours are based on some degree of fact, and so it was with the giant kiwi. A large kiwi *did* live in the rugged mountains of the South Island, but it was not of the proportions claimed for *A. maxima*. It became known to science in August 1871 when Thomas Potts, an ornithologist with the Canterbury Museum, showed two skins of a large *Apteryx* to the Philosophical Institute of Canterbury. Both specimens had been taken high in the ranges of Westland the previous summer by a professional collector. They presented 'such peculiarities' that Potts considered them a new species, which he named *A. haastii*, in honour of Dr Julius von Haast. Potts's judgement was excellent, and the great spotted kiwi, or roa, has remained *A. haastii* to this day.

It took time for some people to accept that *Apteryx haastii* and *A. maxima* were one and the same thing. The hunt for the giant kiwi continued on a smaller scale for a few years after Potts's discovery, and then finally petered out in the late 1880s. Soon afterwards, *A. maxima* slipped quietly into oblivion, despite Buller's unsuccessful attempt to use the name for the Stewart Island kiwi.

The discovery of *A. haastii* did not generate the excitement it deserved, probably because people had been conditioned to expect a much grander bird. But it was grand in its own right; and astonishing that it had avoided capture for so long. Little spotted kiwis had been discovered some 25 years previously, while the South Island brown had been known for at least 60 years. Potts's find marked both the climax and the end of kiwi discovery in New Zealand. The great spotted kiwi, the most handsome of the three species, was surely the greatest prize of them all.

GENERAL DESCRIPTION AND CALLS

Great spotted kiwis live mainly in alpine and subalpine areas of north-west Nelson and Westland. Their surroundings are severe but magnificent; snow-covered peaks, herb fields with rocky outcrops, valleys of red tussock, and mountains clothed in beech forest and alpine shrubs. The birds themselves befit the grandeur of surroundings, both in appearance and behaviour — large, handsome and bold.

Their calls are not quite as powerful as Haast described, but they are loud, carrying several kilometres in still conditions. The calls of females — a series of deep, slow, warbling whistles — possess a haunting quality and are difficult to localise. They seem to linger for a few seconds, so that each successive whistle merges into the one before. The calls of males are shriller and usually of quicker tempo — a warbling, ascending whistle repeated up to twenty times.

The birds are predominately mottled grey, with a varying degree of chestnut on the back. Some are entirely grey, and look like a large little spotted kiwi; others have a distinctly ginger appearance, and from the rear could be mistaken for a brown kiwi. The plumage on the upper parts of their head and neck is charcoal grey, fading to pale grey on the throat and belly. The feathers on their forehead and face are short and dense. Sometimes these become matted with mud, so that they stick out at odd angles, or stained a dull red or brown from contact with soil and rotting wood. Punk hair styles have been in fashion with great spotted kiwis for several million years. The feathers on their back and flanks are up to ten centimetres long and soft to the touch. They lie neatly in place, giving the birds a smooth, rounded outline. As in all kiwis, the feathers are easily dislodged, particularly when the bird is distressed.

Most great spotted kiwis have dark brown legs and toes, but a few have creamy-white ones. Claw colour is variable and changes with age. Chicks start life with black claws, but these start to fade to a horn colour after two or three years, when the bird reaches sexual maturity. The process continues steadily for the rest of their life, so that after a few more years there is little of the original black left, other than a thin stripe down the middle of each claw. This, too, eventually disappears in old age.

Their eyes are dark, small and watery, similar to those of hedgehogs. These appear to be an evolutionary afterthought, but are nevertheless highly functional; the birds can run quickly through thick vegetation, both by day and by night. The ears are placed well back in the skull and are more prominent than the eyes. The birds' sense of hearing is exceptionally good.

Both sexes have the same plumage, but mature females are distinguishable by their larger size and longer bills. A female in prime condition tips the scales at 3.5–4 kilograms, about a kilogram more than its mate. This makes them comparable in weight to the Stewart Island and South Island brown kiwis, and about 500 grams heavier on average than the North Island brown kiwi. Females stand about 50 centimetres tall, and males about 45 centimetres. Their bills are relatively short, at least compared to those of brown kiwis — about 95–105 millimetres in males, and 110–120 millimetres in females. Bill colour is the same in both sexes — a pale ivory suffused with pink, sometimes with a slate-grey hue on the upper mandible. A sparse growth of cat-like whiskers, each about 1–5 centimetres long, surrounds the base of the bill.

Few people have seen great spotted kiwis in the wild, mainly because the birds are nocturnal and live in remote areas. Few specimens are kept in captivity, and none of these are on public display. It is perhaps unfortunate that such a magnificent bird should be so difficult to see. For most people who venture into great spotted kiwi habitat, however, the sight of kiwi footprints on a muddy track or the sound of their haunting calls at night are proof enough of their presence, and rewarding experiences in their own right.

KIWIS

DISTRIBUTION

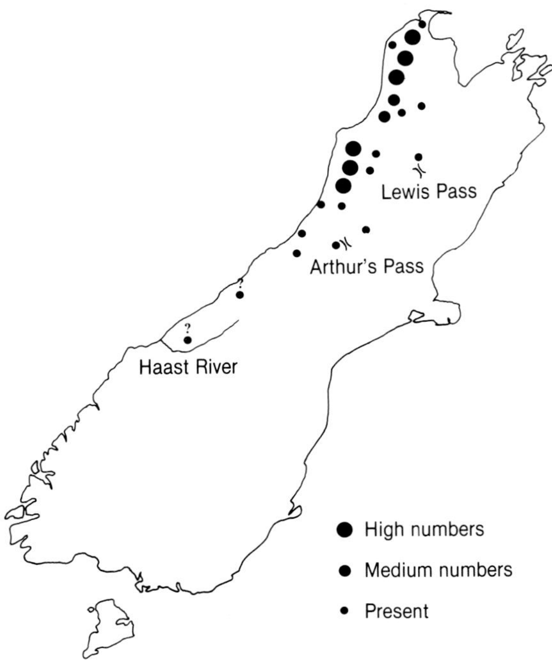

Distribution of great spotted kiwi, *A. haastii*.

Great spotted kiwis are found only in the South Island of New Zealand, mainly west of the Main Divide, from Tasman Bay to south Westland. The southern limit of their range is poorly known. Observers often confuse great spotted kiwi calls with those of South Island brown kiwis, and this makes it very difficult to determine where one species finishes and the other starts. It is fairly certain that great spotted kiwis do not penetrate into Fiordland, even though some specimens in the Canterbury Museum were supposedly collected in Dusky Sound last century. These birds have almost certainly been mislabelled.

Great spotted kiwis spill over to the eastern side of the Main Divide near the Arthur's and Lewis Passes. Recent surveys show that they are present in the headwaters of the Thompson and Poulter Rivers in Canterbury. These birds are not new immigrants from the west, as Falla *et al.* have suggested, since it was in this general area that Julius von Haast heard his giant kiwis more than a century ago. Indeed, a subfossil great spotted kiwi from Pyramid Valley in Canterbury suggests that the birds have been on the eastern side of the alps for at least a thousand years.

Great spotted kiwis are not found on offshore islands. Seven pairs were transferred from north-west Nelson to Little Barrier Island in 1915, but these failed to establish.

STATUS, ABUNDANCE, POPULATION CHANGES

Great spotted kiwis are most numerous in wet, cold, alpine and subalpine forests, 700–1000 metres above sea level. The mountain ranges immediately adjacent to the western coasts of north-west Nelson and Westland seem to be home to the most birds. These mountains intercept the moist westerly winds that sweep in from the Tasman Sea, and receive rain on about 200 days of the year. The forests in their foothills are moist, luxuriant and nearly impenetrable, but give way to more open beech forests at higher altitudes. Mosses and lichens flourish in the wet, cool conditions under the beech — carpeting the ground, enveloping decaying logs, and festooning the roots, trunks and branches of the canopy trees.

It is up here, among the mists and the moss, that great spotted kiwis are most numerous. These favoured areas have four or five pairs of kiwis to each square kilometre. Numbers are much less in the mountains further east, where the rainfall is somewhat lighter and the temperatures are much cooler, and they are generally absent altogether about twenty kilometres from the coast.

Great spotted kiwis are present in some lowland and coastal forests, usually in very low numbers, but the status of both the alpine and lowland populations is unclear. It is not yet known if the birds prefer alpine forest, or whether those that survive there today are remnants of a once extensive population that also flourished in lowland areas. This question is now being tackled by staff of the Department of Scientific and Industrial Research; it is to be hoped that their studies will show that the 8,000 or so great spotted kiwis living in the South Island today are both maintaining their numbers and in no immediate danger of extinction.

GENERAL ECOLOGY

Great spotted kiwi, *A. haastii*, studies. Oil, 1982.

Great spotted kiwis are the least well known of the three kiwi species. New Zealand's early settlers and naturalists wrote little about them, probably because in those days great spotted kiwis were both the rarest and least

Great Spotted
R Harris-Ching

accessible of the three species. In 1955, Oliver summarised in three paragraphs all that had then been learnt about the birds — and only very recently has it become possible to add a few more lines to his account. The new information comes from the north-west Nelson study, in which ten kiwis have been tagged with a small radio transmitter and followed for nine months.

ACTIVITY AND FEEDING ECOLOGY

Great spotted kiwis begin their 'day' in the half-light of dusk, some 30 minutes after sunset, when darkness is thickening on the forest floor but the sky is still tinged with light. In the New Zealand bush, this transition from day to night is often accompanied by a pressing hush, broken only by the last sporadic calls of the day-active birds, and the occasional screech or chirp of the stirring nocturnal animals and insects. Great spotted kiwis emerge into this stillness, and end it with their first calls.

The birds step abruptly out of their daytime shelters, usually without a precautionary glance around, sniff about the entrance for a few seconds, stretch, and then begin the search for the insects, snails, spiders and berries that make up their diet.

Great spotted kiwis, like the other two species, locate their food mainly by smell. The birds walk slowly, gently tapping their bill on the ground in an arc in front, much as a blind person might use a walking stick. They explore most objects in their path fairly carefully, stooping to examine the underside of logs and crevices in tree roots, or stretching to probe clumps of moss and lichen on tree trunks. They often hop up on to fallen logs and probe the rotting wood, and sometimes walk along tree trunks that lean out horizontally from steep hillsides. In this way they can obtain invertebrates that may be a metre or more above ground, seemingly well beyond the reach of a flightless bird.

When they scent food, the birds probe for it, forcing their bill through the substrate with a series of forward and backward rocking motions. Sometimes they swivel round in a full circle at the same time, widening the opening and changing the angle of attack. Once secured, the prey item is carefully and slowly removed, then swallowed with a quick backwards flick of the head. Some large food items such as wetas (a heavyweight cricket) and native earthworms are shaken into smaller bits before being eaten.

Great spotted kiwis have catholic tastes; one of their more unlikely foods is the freshwater crayfish, a small night-feeding lobster that lives in rivers and streams. It was thought until recently that the birds 'fished' for these animals by wading in shallow water and probing for them among the crevices and stones. But it is now clear that they capture them on the forest floor, mainly on very wet nights, when the crayfish abandon their flooded streams and seek refuge under nearby vegetation.

Kiwis are active all night every night, irrespective of weather. They tolerate some appalling conditions — torrential rain, thrashing gales, and biting cold — which force most other nocturnal animals to seek shelter. The birds travel up to three kilometres in a night, through thick undergrowth and tangled gullies, across streams, and up and down steep hillsides. They move almost silently as they go, occasionally rustling a fern frond or snapping a small twig.

They finish their wanderings at dawn in winter, and about one hour after dawn during the short nights of summer. Their last calls on summer mornings often mingle with the dawn chorus of the day birds, just before the sun tinges the mountain tops and whitens the mists in the valleys.

Great spotted kiwi, *A. haastii*, adult males. Pencil, 1981.

Great spotted kiwi, *A. haastii*, running. Oil, 1982.

Auckland 1-1-82
R. Harris-Ching
'Kiwi' Pl. 21

SHELTERS AND DENNING BEHAVIOUR

Great spotted kiwis hide during the daylight hours, usually in a natural chamber under the buttress roots of a living tree. These chambers are typically about one metre wide, half a metre high, and have a roof and walls of roots naturally criss-crossed and interwoven to form a wooden frame. The roots in turn support a thick layer of moss, which plugs the gaps and forms a light-proof cover. Each chamber usually has several small openings at ground level, which the birds may enlarge to get through. The chambers themselves are dingy and damp, sometimes with puddles on the floor. The birds usually carry in enough vegetation to make a small mat, on which they squat during the day, perhaps to keep them off the wet ground.

Great spotted kiwis also shelter in hollow logs, and in underground burrows up to two metres long, which the birds excavate themselves. Sometimes they simply crouch under a thick clump of vegetation. Females do this much more often than males, for reasons that are not yet clear.

Great spotted kiwis usually use a different shelter each day. Each bird has as many as a hundred different shelters in its range, some of which are used at least three or four times a month, others only once or twice a year. Members of bonded pairs often share the same shelter, especially during late winter and spring when breeding starts.

The birds spend most of the day sleeping, with their bill tucked under their tiny wing. They wake from time to time to preen, defecate, stretch, and (in wet weather) shake water off their feathers. They stay in the same shelter throughout the day, unless disturbed. Although bold and aggressive at night, they are very timid by day and will quietly slip away if they hear an animal or person approaching. Indeed, hunters and trampers often say that great spotted kiwis feed during the day, because they have personally seen the birds moving then. But it is fear, not food, that prompts a kiwi to abandon a daylight shelter.

TERRITORIAL BEHAVIOUR

Great spotted kiwis are monogamous. Mates pair for several breeding seasons, and possibly for their entire life. Each pair lives in a territory, which they defend against other kiwis. In favourable areas a pair will require perhaps 25 hectares.

There is little overlap between neighbouring pairs. The birds clearly know the boundaries of territories, although for us these are invisible and bear little relationship with any obvious features of the landscape. Neighbouring pairs are sometimes separated by a stream, but many territories span both sides of quite large waterways.

It is not yet known how the birds defend such large areas, but it seems that calling is involved. Members of a pair call five to twenty times most nights, partly to maintain contact with each other but also to tell other kiwis that their patch of forest is already occupied. Tests with taped calls show that territory owners respond very aggressively to the call of a stranger. The resident male usually replies immediately the 'intruder' stops calling, then starts running towards it. His approach is direct, bold and threatening: he closes at full speed, tumbling and bouncing down hillsides, crashing through undergrowth with the noise of a stampeding deer. The pitter-patter of his feet can be heard distinctly in the final twenty metres of his approach. He comes out of the darkness in battle mode — head held high, bill pointed down, and feathers fluffed out to increase his apparent size.

A real intruder with the slightest sense of self-preservation would probably flee at this point. But the tension soon dissipates when the resident discovers that the threat is nothing more than a person holding a tape recorder. He usually sniffs around their feet, kicks them half-heartedly on the leg, then wanders off into the undergrowth, content that the enemy has been vanquished.

Females also respond to taped calls, but with much more caution. They usually approach the intruder slowly and silently, picking their way carefully through the undergrowth. Often the sound of sniffing, audible up to two metres, is the first indication of their arrival. They flee at the slightest movement, run about 50 metres, then stop and call several times, perhaps to summon the help of their mate.

Some territorial encounters do involve righting. One radio-tagged male in the north-west Nelson study was killed by another kiwi, probably in a dispute over space. The intruder struck the resident on the back, driving a claw into its spine. It then kicked the crippled bird repeatedly, stripping feathers off its back, tearing its skin and causing massive internal bruising so that death occurred a few hours later.

Encounters of this type involving injury or death are rare, however. Most territories would change ownership only when the resident male dies or is sick or injured.

BREEDING

Great spotted kiwis are similar to the other two species in that they produce an extremely large egg (equivalent to about 20 per cent of the female's weight), lay in early spring, and nest in burrows and natural holes. But there the similarity ends.

Brown and little spotted kiwis are heaviest in late winter, just before breeding, but great spotted kiwis are fairly skinny then. Their seasonal peak is some five months earlier, in late autumn. Their weight declines by about a quarter from May to early spring, levels off in midsummer, then soars back up in March and April. Food is so scarce during winter that the birds have to metabolise fat to meet their energy requirements. Despite this, females still manage to produce their large, energy-rich egg in early spring — and they do it by mobilising the rest of the reserves that they packed away some five months previously. Thus the egg is technically made in autumn, but laid in spring.

There is only enough stored energy for one egg — this is their clutch for the year. They cannot re-lay if this egg fails, nor add a second egg at some later stage, even though males are perfectly capable of incubating two. Indeed, the energy balance of the female is so precarious that there is probably little or no laying in years with poor autumns or severe winters. By comparison, brown kiwis in some North Island forests can find enough food to lay five eggs in a breeding season.

The inability of female great spotted kiwis to produce more than one egg has an interesting side effect. They do not have to feed furiously after they have laid, because the task of producing a second egg is impossible, so they help instead with incubation, taking over when the male goes out to feed. In contrast, female brown and little spotted kiwis cannot afford to give up feeding time to incubate, otherwise they would reduce their ability to lay replacement and second clutches; in both of these species only the male incubates.

Chick A. Haasti
at about 10 days.
2/3

GREAT SPOTTED KIWI

By sharing incubation, great spotted kiwis seldom leave their egg unattended and exposed to the cold night air. This in turn probably means that the incubation period is shorter than in the other species, and their eggs suffer less predation, because there is always one parent present to drive off robbers. As yet, however, we do not know the exact incubation period and breeding success of great spotted kiwis in the wild. The behaviour and development of chicks are also unknown. But chicks probably become independent about three weeks after hatching, as do those of the other species.

CONCLUSION

Dramatic changes have taken place in the New Zealand landscape since Potts first described the great spotted kiwi in 1871. Most of the lowland forests have been cleared, deer and other herbivores have spread from one end of the country to the other, and predators now live cheek by jowl with the native fauna. The human population has increased from a few thousand to over three million, and the mountains — once remote and uninhabited — are now the weekend playground of skiers, trampers, hunters, and fishermen.

Great spotted kiwis are one of the few mainland species that have hardly been touched by these changes. They see a few more people than they did in Potts's day — but transients only, who all but disappear with the coming of winter. Their corner of the South Island is still much the same as it was when the first Europeans arrived — too inhospitable for people, too tough for farming and commercial forestry, and too tough for some of the mammals that have ravaged the landscape elsewhere.

Thus, evolution has handed out an odd but fair deal to great spotted kiwis. On the one hand, the birds have to struggle from one day to the next to survive in their harsh land; but on the other hand, it is the harshness itself that has so far made their home secure. And with luck, it should continue to protect these magnificent birds for the foreseeable future.

BIBLIOGRAPHY

Buller, W. L. 1868. Essay on the ornithology of New Zealand. *Transactions and Proceedings of the New Zealand Institute*, 1: 213–31.

Buller, W. L. 1891. On the large kiwi from Stewart Island (*Apteryx maxima*). *Transactions and Proceedings of the New Zealand Institute*, 24: 91–92.

Falla, R. A., Sibson, R. B. and Turbott, E. G. 1979. *The new guide to the birds of New Zealand.* Collins, Auckland and London. 247 pp.

McLennan, J. A. 1988. Breeding of North Island Brown Kiwi, *Apteryx australis mantelli*, in Hawke's Bay, New Zealand. *New Zealand Journal of Ecology*, 11: 89–97.

Oliver, W. R. B. 1955. *New Zealand Birds.* A. H. & A. W. Reed, Wellington, Sydney and London. pp. 55–56.

Potts, T. H. 1871. Notes on a new species of *Apteryx.* (*A. Haastii*, Potts). *Transactions and Proceedings of the New Zealand Institute*, 4: 204– 5.

Reid, B. and Williams, G. R. 1975: The kiwi. In: *Biogeography and Ecology in New Zealand.* Kuschel, G., ed. Junk, The Hague.

Reid, B., Ordish, R. G. and Harrison, M. 1982. An analysis of the gizzard contents of 50 North Island brown kiwis, *Apteryx australis mantelli*, and notes on feeding observations. *New Zealand Journal of Ecology*, 5: 76–85.

Hutton, F. W. 1871. *Catalogue of the birds of New Zealand with diagnoses of the species.* James Hughes, Printer, Lambton Quay, Wellington. 85 pp.

Verreaux, J. 1856. *Comtes Rendus Academic Science*: xliii. p. 841.

Great spotted kiwi, *A. haastii*, chicks. Pencil, 1988.

7

THE LITTLE SPOTTED KIWI

LITTLE SPOTTED KIWI

Apteryx owenii Gould, 1847.

Apteryx owenii Gould, 1847, *Proceedings of the Zoological Society*, p. 94.
Apteryx mollis Potts, 1873, *Transactions of the New Zealand Institute*, 5, p. 196.
Apteryx oweni occidentalis Rothschild, 1893, *Bulletin of the British Ornithologist's Club*, 1, p. 61.

DESCRIPTION

Head small; neck thick; body cone-shaped; tail not visible; wings rudimentary; feet and legs sturdy; bill long, slender and almost straight with tip of upper mandible projecting over lower and with nostrils at tip; base of bill surrounded by whiskers; plumage shaggy and hair-like, each feather with a single shaft and unlinked barbs; head and neck yellowish grey, remainder of plumage grey with mottled appearance and feathers banded with blackish brown; feet and legs off-white to pale pink; claws usually white, sometimes dark; bill flesh-coloured; iris black.

Sexes alike, although female is larger than male; young, similar to adults, only smaller.

DISTINGUISHING FEATURES

Small size and mottled appearance distinguish this species from *Apteryx australis*; small size and lack of chestnut hue on the back separate it from *A. haastii*.

MEASUREMENTS

Length: 400 mm.
Male: bill 63–72 mm; tarsus 65–79 mm; mid-toe 60–64 mm.
Female: bill 75–94 mm; tarsus 69–87 mm; mid-toe 60–76 mm.

EGGS

Clutch one to two; colour white; 105 × 68 mm to 113 × 76 mm.

RANGE

Kapiti Island; possibly D'Urville Island and remote forests of the South Island.

STATUS AND DISTRIBUTION

The little spotted kiwi is the smallest and rarest of the kiwis. Today, all but a few individuals reside on Kapiti Island, a 2,000-hectare nature reserve in Cook Strait, and with only one population on one island, the species is considered to be endangered.

Little spotted kiwis were, until at least 500 years ago, widespread in both the North and South Islands. However, by the time of European settlement, some 150 years ago, they had all but gone from the North Island. The causes of their disappearance in the North Island are uncertain. The Maori had cleared by burning as much as half of the North Island's original forest, the principal habitat of kiwis, but large areas of forest remained untouched. Kiwis

Little spotted kiwi, *Apteryx owenii*. Oil (detail), 1989.

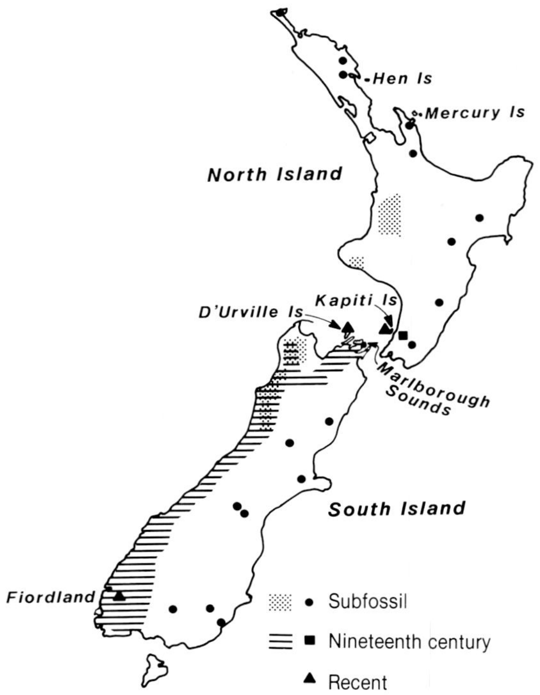

were hunted by the Maori, and the Maori dog may well have roamed the forest near villages, but neither would be likely to cause more than local extinctions. In the South Island, little spotted kiwis were still widespread in the north and west early this century, and their disappearance coincides with the spread of introduced mammalian predators, particularly the stoat (*Mustela erminea*).

It is possible that a few little spotted kiwis remain in remote forests of the South Island, but the last specimen was recovered in 1938. Since then, the only confirmed record was of some (recently deposited) leg bones found in Fiordland in 1973.

Little spotted kiwis were also present on at least two offshore islands besides Kapiti: Cooper Island in Fiordland and D'Urville Island in the Marlborough Sounds (Figure 1). They have disappeared from the former, but a few may still persist on D'Urville Island. One female and three males have been found there in the last ten years. All were caught and moved away from the stoats, cats, pigs and dogs now present.

FIGURE 1 Past and present distribution of little spotted kiwis together with the locality of islands to which birds have recently been transferred.

Until recently, it was believed the population on Kapiti Island originated from a transfer from Jacksons Bay, south Westland, in 1912. Searches of government reports and files indicate confusion between species of kiwis and that it was probably brown kiwis that were liberated on the island. It is more likely that the little spotted kiwi was native to the island, as it was to the adjacent mainland on either side of Cook Strait. Kapiti was connected to the mainland as recently as 12,000 years ago. However, it is also possible that the birds were liberated on the island when it had a large Maori population, 150 or more years ago.

Much of the information on little spotted kiwis comes from a 1980–85 study on Kapiti Island, when the size and health of the population were investigated, along with the bird's diet and habitat requirements, its social behaviour and breeding biology.

DESCRIPTION

Little spotted kiwis are only about half the size of the other two kiwi species. They stand about 25 centimetres tall. The larger and heavier females weigh on average 1,330 grams (range 1,010–1,660), whereas the males average 1,200 grams (range 880–1,384). Bills of little spotted kiwis are both shorter (females, 85 millimetres, range 75.1–93.8; males, 68 millimetres, range 63.5–71.5) and less curved than those of the larger kiwis. As with all kiwis, the tail has disappeared externally, and the wings are tiny (40–50 millimetres long), almost naked, and hidden in the body plumage. The legs and feet are off-white to pale pink, with claws that are usually white, sometimes darker. Chicks hatch as fully feathered miniatures of the adults, weighing about 150 grams and with bills about 38 millimetres long.

The plumage of little spotted kiwis is grey, mottled with white, and has the same appearance in males, females, juveniles and chicks. Individual feathers have a single shaft and unlinked barbs, which give the plumage a shaggy appearance. The feathers have two white bands (one in chicks) and are sometimes lighter in colour at the base and the tip. The plumage is readily distinguishable from brown kiwis, whose brown feathers are streaked lengthways, but the plumage of great spotted kiwis can only be distinguished by the rufous tinge to their backs. Immature great spotted kiwis can easily be confused with little spotted kiwis, and have been frequently mislabelled in museum collections.

The loud calls of kiwis are the best clues of their presence in a locality, and the species and sex can usually be distinguished by a trained listener. Male little spotted kiwis have a high-pitched whistle, whereas females have a lower-pitched, strongly trilled whistle. The calls of both sexes carry for hundreds of metres.

HABITAT AND DIET

On Kapiti Island, little spotted kiwis live in temperate, evergreen, broadleaf forest and scrub. Rainfall averages 1,000 millimetres annually but the island rises steeply to 500 metres above sea level, and the dampness of the upper forest is increased by a cloud zone. Large areas of the island were burnt or cleared for horticulture and grazing up until the early years of this century, but the forest is now regenerating over most of the island. The large population of kiwis, estimated to exceed a thousand birds, is distributed throughout the resulting mosaic of vegetation types.

Little spotted kiwis, like the other kiwi species, are omnivorous, eating both invertebrates and the fruit of forest trees and shrubs. They find their food both in the forest litter and by probing the soil to the full depth of their bills.

Analysis of faecal samples showed that earthworms (Annelida), cockchafer beetle larvae (Scarabidae), caterpillars (Lepidoptera), cranefly larvae (Tipulidae) and spiders (Aranaea) were the foods eaten most frequently (Figure 2). Larger adult beetles, up to 40 millimetres long, wetas (Orthoptera), cicada larvae (Hemiptera), and millipedes (Diplopoda) were also often eaten. Some fruit, particularly that of the hinau tree (*Elaeocarpus dentatus*) and the fleshy fruits of some creepers and low bushes, made up the diet. Sporangia (fruiting bodies) on the underside of fern fronds were also frequently found in the droppings, but it is uncertain if these and other types of plant material were ingested deliberately by the kiwis or if they were picked up incidentally with other food. Chicks also search the forest litter and probe the soil for food. In faecal samples from chicks, the smaller invertebrates — cranefly larvae, millipedes, earthworms, caterpillars and a cave weta (Raphidophoridae) — were found, as well as fern sporangia.

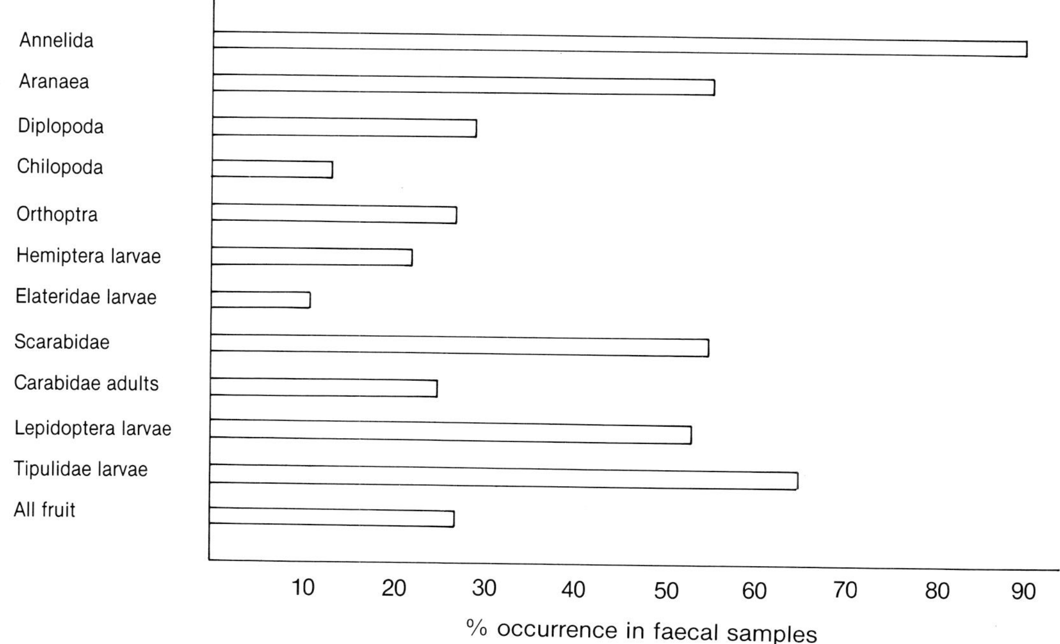

FIGURE 2 Principal components of the diet of little spotted kiwis on Kapiti Island derived from % occurrence of food items in faecal samples. (After Jolly and Ordish, in prep.)

SOCIAL BEHAVIOUR

Kiwis, unlike other birds, appear to sense their environment by sound and smell rather than by sight; this also applies to the way in which they communicate with each other. They have few visual displays, and these nocturnal forest dwellers rely more on their calls both to maintain territories and for contact between individuals of a pair. At close quarters, smell also seems to play a part, as a kiwi, called in by a taped or whistled imitation of its call, often raises its bill and can be heard sniffing. Kiwis fight with their feet, and fighting is accompanied by jumping, kicking, snorting and bill snapping. Wild chases often ensue, usually terminating with the loud calls of the victor. Although their small eyes indicate poor vision, kiwis can certainly see well enough to run at high speed through dense undergrowth. But little spotted kiwis are less aggressive and raucous than the larger kiwis, and were well described by the early New Zealand naturalist Richard Henry as the 'shy and gentle' little kiwi.

Little spotted kiwis are dispersed in strongly territorial pairs. Neither adult nor immature intruders are tolerated within a pair's territory at any time of the year.

A pair will often share their daytime shelter burrow. Shortly before emerging, they may grunt to each other for several minutes. Sometimes the grunting continues for a few minutes after they leave the nest, but thereafter they go their own way in search of food. From time to time one will run towards the other's call, and they may then stand next to each other, stretching upwards with bills raised vertically. A more spectacular display accompanies copulation. Both birds stand with bills crossed and pointed downwards while they shuffle around each other for up to 20 minutes, giving soft grunts.

In spite of apparently having few displays, pair bonds are strong and long-lasting. Twelve pairs of study birds were all still in their original pairings and in the same territories of up to two hectares four years after they were banded. Immature birds, on the other hand, are transitory as they are forced from territory to territory by the adults.

BREEDING BIOLOGY AND NESTING SUCCESS

Breeding begins in early spring when noticeably heavy females were found. Female little spotted kiwis can weigh up to 1,900 grams (490 grams more than their normal weight) when heavy with an egg. The first nests of the season were found in September, and, once started, all the study pairs had nested within three weeks. Breeding also extended into November and December with replacement nests.

Of 31 nests found, 22 were in burrows up to 80 centimetres long by 15 centimetres wide, dug into steep banks. Six nests were in existing cavities as much as 200 centimetres long, in logs or rotting tree stumps. The other three nests were in thickets of vegetation. The kiwis used a new site for each nesting, and although each pair had in its territory 30 to 40 long burrows or cavities, their nests were sometimes in burrows as short as 20 centimetres. Another surprising feature of their nest sites was that none was dug out before laying; all were in old burrows or unaltered cavities. Nevertheless, most of the nests were well hidden, as the kiwis usually completely covered the entrances of shorter burrows with twigs and leaves. Nest cavities were sometimes lined with material from the forest floor, but were not adorned with feathers or moss.

The eggs of little spotted kiwis are even larger (110 × 70 millimetres) and heavier (300 grams), relative to the birds' size, than those of the other kiwi species. They are obovate in shape and white with a smooth, thin shell (0.4 millimetres). Nineteen one-egg and two two-egg clutches were found, but early loss of many nests may have prevented more two-egg clutches being laid. Because the egg is so large, only one can develop within the female's ovary at a time and there is a two- to three-week interval before the second egg is laid. During the five-year study, six pairs replaced nests that failed early in incubation after an interval of one to two months, but those that hatched clutches did not lay again.

Only the male attends the nest during the long incubation period of about 70 days. He takes over from the female the day after laying and, although he may miss one or two complete days in the first ten days after laying, he is on the nest thereafter every day and part of the night for up to 21 hours at a time. The egg is left unattended at night for up to ten hours and must cool considerably. This cooling probably explains the much longer incubation period than would be expected for an egg of this size.

Little spotted kiwi eggs are exceptionally rich in yolk, and after hatching, the chick feeds from its yolk sac for a few days. In fact, adult kiwis have never been seen to feed their chicks. After a few days the highly precocious chicks emerge from the nest and, independently of the adults, begin probing for food themselves. The chicks share the nest with the male parent during the day for about three weeks after hatching. Although the female renews her interest in the nest at about hatching time, neither parent gives the chicks any more than a loose escort at night. Chicks are usually seen on their own in the forest. They emerge from the nest before the male up to an hour before dusk and return later than him, up to 40 minutes after dawn. It seems to be the male who abandons the nest first, but the chick usually spends only one last day in the nest alone before finding its own daytime shelter, often in the open at the base of a tree, or in thickets of undergrowth.

The breeding strategy of the little spotted kiwi is geared, then, to a low rate of production of eggs that are designed to produce a well-developed, highly precocious chick with the best possible chances of surviving factors such as food shortage or unfavourable weather. But in the three-year study of breeding success on Kapiti Island, only three eggs hatched from 22 nests monitored, and probably only two chicks left these nests. As well, some of the eight or nine pairs studied were known to have bred, but lost their eggs so quickly that we did not find their nests. Even though all pairs bred each year, an average only 0.08 chicks were reared per pair per year. That is, any one pair would rear only one chick in thirteen years.

The weka (*Gallirallus australis*), a flightless New Zealand rail introduced to Kapiti Island in 1896, made a considerable contribution to these losses. Wekas were seen at eight of the nests eating the eggs, but probably at least two-thirds of the eggs were taken by wekas, judging by the type of damage to the eggs and the disturbance to the nests. Wekas persistently returned to the nests until they were able to take the egg, from under the incubating kiwi on two occasions, and at night after the kiwi had left, on another two. The highly independent chicks are also vulnerable, particularly as they are active at dawn and dusk, but we recorded only one probable predation of a chick by a weka.

Even though the kiwi is a long-lived bird (up to twenty years in captivity), and nested annually during the study on Kapiti Island, these high nest losses, together with the likely high loss of newly independent young, would, if sustained, result in a population decline. It seems incongruous that wekas could have a major impact on the kiwis, as the two species have lived together

Little spotted kiwi, *A. owenii*.
Oil on prepared wood panel, 1980.

on Kapiti Island for 90 years and used to occur together on the mainland. Two factors could explain this anomaly. Wekas are currently at very high densities on Kapiti Island, but if the population has fluctuated, as some have done on the mainland, the predation pressure on kiwi nests could at times be much less. The kiwi population could then be replenished at times of low weka density.

Second, in comparison with the mainland, most of the forest on Kapiti Island is young and has little ground cover, with few logs and thickets of vegetation. This may make the nests easier for wekas to find than on the mainland. In young forest on Kapiti Island, nearly 70 per cent of the study nests were probably lost to wekas, but in older forest, where nests were better disguised, only 40 per cent of nests were lost to wekas. All three eggs that hatched were in nests in older forest.

MANAGEMENT

Although Kapiti Island is a reserve and the population of little spotted kiwis there is large, the species is at risk by being confined to only one island. Apart from weka predation, fire, disease or the introduction of mammalian predators could deplete the population. Island transfers and captive breeding are the likely tools for reducing the species vulnerability. Captive breeding provides an opportunity both to study the bird's breeding biology and to develop methods of husbandry in case of a disaster in the wild population. Little spotted kiwis bred successfully at the Mount Bruce National Wildlife Centre in the mid-1970s, but it was not until 1989 that another chick was reared successfully, this time at the Otorohanga National Kiwi Centre.

Part of the research programme on little spotted kiwis involves selecting suitable islands for transfers. Islands of at least 200 hectares, and preferably more than 500, in size are needed to establish a population with long-term viability. Eight likely islands have been checked for mammalian predators, particularly stoats, an adequate food supply of invertebrates, presence of water, and quality of vegetation.

Two islands, Red Mercury (210 hectares) off the Coromandel Peninsula, and Hen (480 hectares), off Whangarei Heads, were selected, and little spotted kiwis were transferred there from Kapiti Island in 1983 and 1988. It is too early to report on the Hen Island transfer, but on Red Mercury, probably all twelve birds transferred have survived for three years since their release. Breeding has yet to be confirmed. One of the little spotted kiwis removed from D'Urville Island in 1980 died in captivity, and a second died on Maud Island in the Marlborough Sounds. The survivor, together with two birds from Kapiti Island and another bird found on D'Urville Island in 1987, was transferred to Long Island (110 hectares) in the Marlborough Sounds in 1981 and 1987 in an attempt to preserve any unique genetic characters of the D'Urville population. All birds on Long Island have survived and successful breeding has been confirmed. But it will only be with a transfer of birds to an island much larger than these three, and with the development of a population similar in size to the one on Kapiti, that the species will have a more assured future.

ACKNOWLEDGEMENTS

Rogan Colbourne worked with me on the research programme on little spotted kiwis and shared the brunt of the field work. Karen Baird, Roger Collins, Paul Jansen, Paul Kane and Brian Lloyd, together with other staff of

Little spotted kiwi, *A. owenii*, studies. Pencil, 1989.

the New Zealand Wildlife Service and volunteers, made major contributions to the field work.

Dr Phil Moors, Don Newman and Dr Murray Williams reviewed an earlier draft of the manuscript. Dr Williams also contributed many valuable ideas during the study.

BIBLIOGRAPHY

Body, D. R. and Reid, B. 1987. The lipid, fatty acid and amino acid composition of ratite eggs from three different species of kiwis *Apterys australis australis*, *A. haastii*, and *A. owenii* bred in captivity on the same diet. *Biochem, System, and Ecol.* 15: 625–8.

Calder, W. A. III. 1978. The kiwi, a case of compensating divergencies from allometric predictions. In: Piper, J. (ed.) *Respiratory Function in Birds, Adult and Embryonic*: 239–42. Berlin, Spring-Verlag.

Davidson, J. 1979. Archaic middens of the Coromandel region: a review. In: Anderson, D. (ed.) *Birds of a Feather*: 183–202.

Handley, J. W. 1896. Notes on some species of birds. *Transactions and Proceedings of the New Zealand Institute,* 28: 360–7.

Henry, R. 1903. *The Habits of the Flightless Birds of New Zealand.* Wellington, Government Printer. 88 pp.

Hill, S. and Hill, J. 1987. *Richard Henry of Resolution Island.* Dunedin, McIndoe. 364 pp.

Jolly, J. N. and Ordish, R. G. (in prep.). The fruit and invertebrate diet of the little spotted kiwi (*Apteryx owenii*) on Kapiti and D'Urville Islands.

Jolly, J. N. 1989. A field study of the breeding biology of the little spotted kiwi (*Apteryx owenii*) with emphasis on the causes of nest failures. *Journal of the Royal Society of New Zealand*, 19: 433–48.

Kinsky, F. C. 1971. The consistent presence of paired ovaries in the kiwi (*Apteryx*) with some discussion of this condition in other birds. *J. Ornithol.* 112: 334–57.

Millener, P. R. 1981. Quaternary Avifauna of the North Island, New Zealand. PhD thesis. University of Auckland. 897 pp.

Rahn, H. and Ar, A. 1974. The avian egg: incubation time and water loss. *Condor*, 76: 147–52.

Reid, B. 1970. Birds of the 'Takahe Study Area'. *Notornis*, 17(1): 56–61.

Scarlett, R. J. 1979. Avifauna and man. In: Anderson, A. (ed.). *Birds of a Feather*: 75–101.

Stevens, G. R. 1974. *Rugged Landscape: The Geology of Central New Zealand.* Wellington, Reed. 286 pp.

Williams, G. R. and Given, D. R. 1981. *The Red Data Book of New Zealand.* Wellington, Nature Conservation Council. 175 pp.

8

KIWIS IN A PINE FOREST HABITAT

Until recently the kiwi has never really had a fair deal: it was considered an anomalous bird, a primitive relict of many million years ago and a dumb, blind, nocturnal flightless creature, burdened by excessively sized olfactory organs and equipped with nostrils weirdly positioned at the tip of the long, slightly curved bill. The scientists of the latter half of the nineteenth century spent much time arguing about the validity of the various described forms and species of kiwi, and this is not surprising when you note the variability in plumage that occurs within one population in one forest. The taxonomic battle went on for a long time on the basis of anatomical and morphological differences, and even today scientists are not quite sure who is who and what lives where, although the research methods now involve the latest technology in blood analysis and other aspects of physiology and biochemistry.

Scientific data obtained in the last century ranged from descriptions of the underside of kiwis' feet to a dry remark in Buller's book on the history of the birds of New Zealand, that the skin of an adult male *Apteryx* is more like that of a mammal and that it is so thick that a pair of light shoes might easily be made of it. Buller's chapters on kiwis have formed the basis of our knowledge of these birds for almost a century. His book not only describes hunting parties and improved methods of catching kiwis (kiwi hunting with dogs is much easier: 40 birds and nine eggs within one week!), it also gives useful hints on how to skin and process kiwis during a collecting expedition in the bush. Observations on the behaviour of kiwis were also noted:

> One of the women produced a newly-hatched chick from her bosom (where it was kept for warmth) and gave it to me. This young bird at first seemed very weakly and on being turned loose in my room assumed the posture shown in my sketch, and remained perfectly motionless till darkness came on, when it assumed quite a lively rôle — running about the room and gently tapping with its bill . . . After sketching the likeness of this defenceless chick (which proved to be a male) I sacrificed his little life on the sacred altar of science and made a pretty cabinet specimen of the skin.

However, Buller and his contemporaries were not only interested in pretty little taxonomic specimens; in the process of skinning and mounting the birds the stomach contents were sometimes examined, albeit in a cursory manner. Identifiable remains of the kiwi's diet included a variety of insect species, some fruits of native trees, quartz pebbles, and the 'egg' of the great earthworm Toke-tipa. This last food item tied in with an earlier observation by Buller in which he saw one of the inmates of the aviary, a recently captured female, extract a large earthworm from the soil. He was able to witness the occasion because the worm in question emits a bright phosphorescent light when it is disturbed at night. His delightful little story describes how the kiwi carefully drew the delicacy out of the ground, without pulling roughly or breaking it, and then smashed it up and devoured it in a spectacular bright green lightshow.

In the first half of the twentieth century very little substantial material was published on kiwis. Apart from a series of experiments which showed some evidence that kiwis are able to detect earthworms in the soil by smell alone, and some anecdotes on the behaviour of captive birds, no real progress was made and Buller's scriptures were still gospel. In the 1950s and 1960s occasional observations both from the field and from captive birds merely supported previous findings and hypotheses.

In the 1970s kiwi research finally started to take off. However, apart from some good work carried out by enthusiastic members of the Otorohanga Zoological Society on their captive birds, most studies were confined to the laboratory, an environment where scientists can comfortably carry out investigations within the 9 a.m. to 5 p.m. limits of Public Service timesheets. Intricate measurements revealed enormous amounts of physiological and biochemical data on the kiwi's body mass, its eggs and the yolk contents thereof, the amount of energy stored in newly hatched chicks, as well as theories on the phylogenetic relationship of kiwis to other flightless bird families around the world.

We must bear in mind that all this trivial research was going on at a time when the conservation movement in New Zealand was growing, both in numbers and in political strength. Buller had already expressed concern about the diminishing numbers of kiwis at the end of last century, and by the 1970s the situation had certainly not improved. Conservationists were stressing the importance of retention of natural, unmodified habitats for our native flora and fauna in general, and for rare and endangered species in particular. The kiwi, which over the past decades had affectionately been adopted by New Zealanders as their national emblem, had indeed slowly become one of these rare life forms. This rather 'primitive' bird, with its alleged strong dependence on natural habitats, was dwindling in numbers in the face of further habitat reduction by conversion of native forests and bush into sylvicultural and agricultural development projects, which ecologists considered to be 'biological deserts'. In view of all this, and the fact that virtually no ecological data on kiwi populations were available, the situation looked grim.

In 1979 kiwis suddenly hit the headlines with the publication of a New Zealand Forest Service report that surprised ecologists and conservationists. An estimated 450 to 500 North Island brown kiwis were believed to inhabit a nearly 3,000-hectare, predominantly exotic pine forest in the Bay of Islands, Northland. Moreover, the report stated that kiwis could not only sustain themselves in pure monocultures of pines, they were also able to maintain their numbers in the face of the rather drastic disturbances that are part and parcel of exotic sylviculture, such as clear-felling and burning. The survey in Waitangi State Forest, which led to the publication of the report, was carried out by Harold Corbett, a forestry student, in liaison with the New Zealand Forest Service and the Wildlife Service. The census method employed by Corbett was a series of random visits to 112 different fixed 'listening stations', where he systematically counted kiwi calls and established the more or less exact positions of the calling birds. After plotting all calling birds on a map, he obtained a fair idea of the locations of the pairs and territories; some areas

Pine forest habitat of North Island brown kiwi, *A. a. mantelli*.
Photo: Jaan Voot

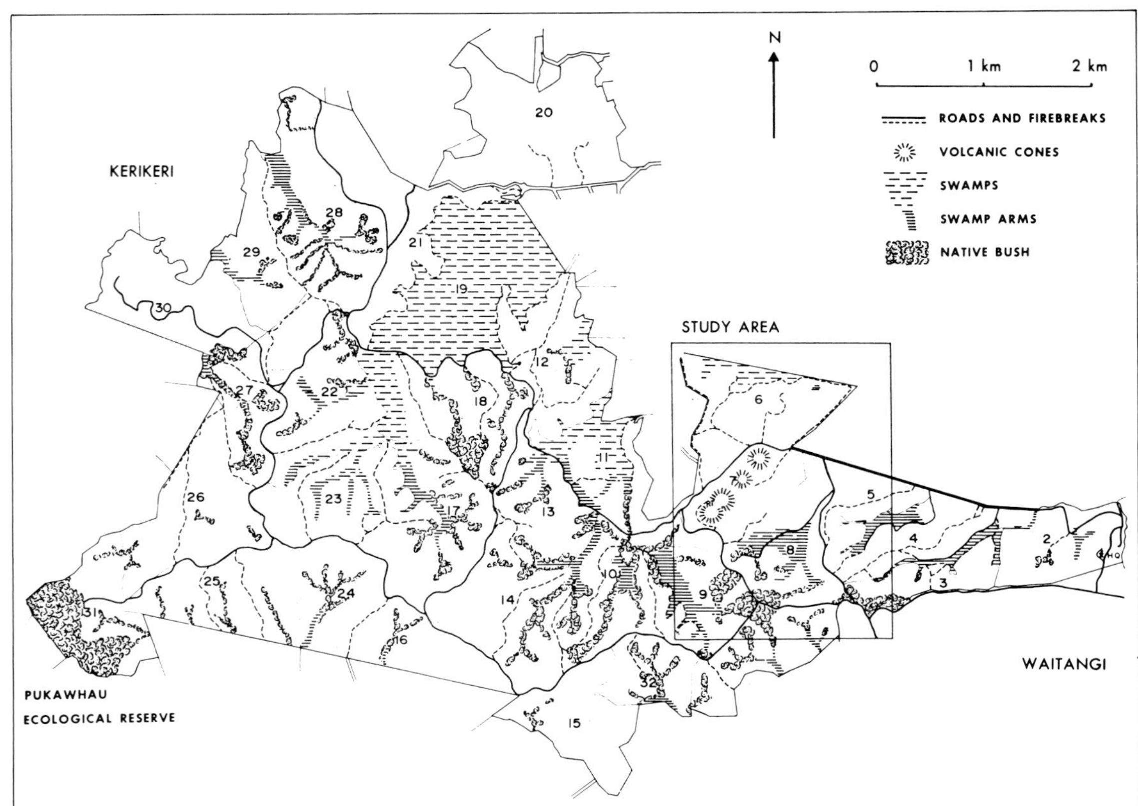

FIGURE 1 Map of Waitangi State Forest (Northland) showing main habitat types and location of study area.

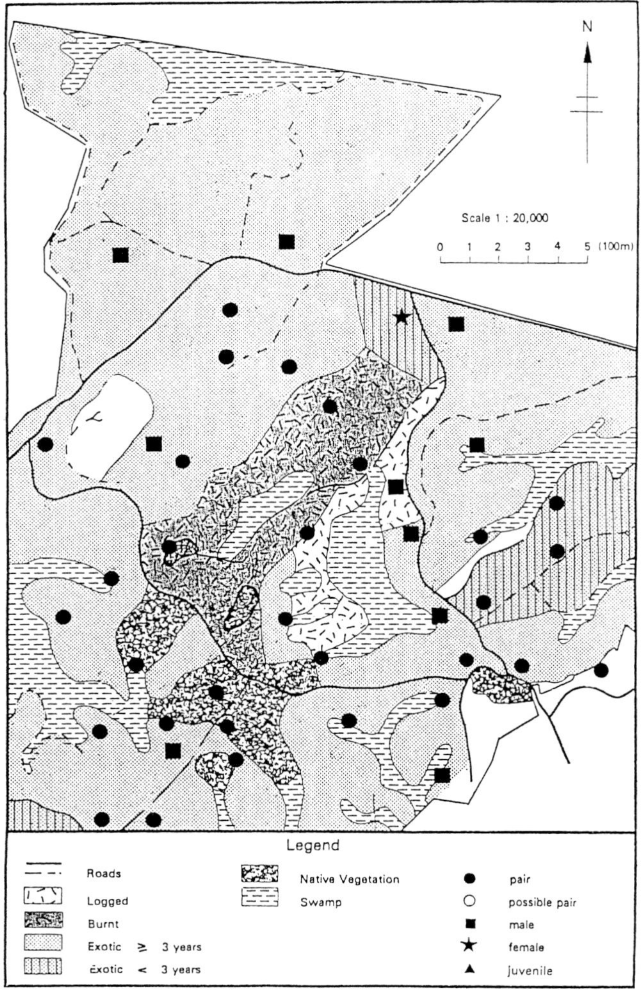

FIGURE 2 Distribution of kiwis in study area after vocalisation census by Corbett in 1978.

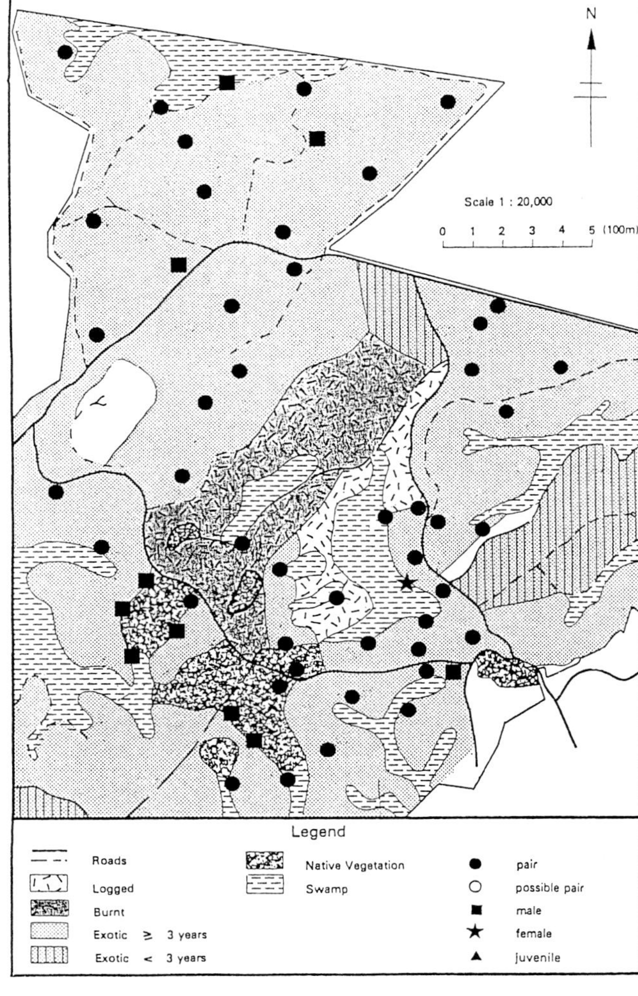

FIGURE 3 Distribution of kiwis in study area after intensified vocalisation census during study in 1981.

showed relatively more kiwis per hectare than other areas in Waitangi Forest.

The Forest Service was in those days the subject of much criticism from conservationists about management policies for the indigenous state forests (selective logging, clear-felling of native forests, conversion into exotics, etc.) and the Waitangi kiwis posed something of a problem. On one hand, the high population density of kiwis in a pine forest is extremely valuable publicity, but on the other hand, interested parties might wish to interfere with or change the exotic sylvicultural practices employed. The ultimate fear, however, was that Waitangi State Forest would be declared a kiwi sanctuary! A continuation of research into the Waitangi kiwis was decided in 1980, and in February 1981, Rogan Colbourne and I started our employment with the New Zealand Forest Service on a contract basis. It certainly was not easy for two energetic young ecologists, dedicated to the principles of conservation, to blend in with the somewhat formal staff of a government department that was constantly under scrutiny from the conservation lobby.

Our initial objectives were drawn up by our Wildlife Service supervisor and involved the following research topics: a check on Corbett's data to monitor any change in numbers since his survey in 1978; an attempt to determine whether the erratic pattern of kiwi distribution in the forest was related to differences in food supply; and a study of the kiwi's diet (via faeces analysis) and feeding behaviour (for example, utilisation of the native bush gullies that intersect the pine stands). It will be noted that these objectives exclude any physical contact with the kiwis themselves!

Our first week in the forest was spent familiarising ourselves with the area and selecting a 350-hectare study area where most of our research would be concentrated. We also set up fourteen food-survey transects in various parts of the forest, where regular soil and litter samples were taken to determine the amount and variety of insect food available to kiwis.

Waitangi State Forest is, by New Zealand standards, a relatively small forest. Of the almost 3,000 hectares, 2,000 are planted in exotic trees, mostly radiata pine (*Pinus radiata*) and southern pine (*Pinus elliottii*). The rest is left as native bush of varying quality, especially in the steep gullies, and there are sometimes extensive swamps in the valleys. Most of the forest's topography consists of a series of steep ridges and gullies, comprising a very heavy podsolised clay which tends to be extremely muddy in winter and rock-hard during the dry summer months. Some flat areas with volcanic cones are situated in the eastern part of the forest and these were included in our study area (see Figure 1). The undergrowth in the Waitangi pine stands is rather variable. Some compartments have none, others are almost impenetrable with gorse, bracken and manuka. Generally, an older pine plantation allows easier access than a younger one. After thinning, which usually occurs when the trees have been growing for about eleven years, the canopy opens up, but access on the ground is almost impossible for human beings. The thinned logs are left criss-cross on the forest floor to decompose, and these become slippery and hazardous (thinning to waste). Kiwis, however, appear to have no problem moving about in those compartments.

Our field work commenced with an intensive survey of the resident kiwi population in our study area, involving many dark nights of long waits on forest roads and tracks. When two observers armed with torches, compasses and synchronised watches are situated 100 to 200 metres apart on roads and fire breaks in the forest, cross-bearings can be obtained that lead to the accurate positions of calling birds. It soon became apparent that there were almost twice as many kiwis in our study area than Corbett detected via his ten-minute bird count (Figures 2 and 3). In fact, compartment 6, which did not yield any kiwis in 1978, was found to contain at least eighteen birds during our vocalisation census in autumn 1981. But that was not all. The intensive survey yielded other interesting observations, and I suppose we may have been quite lucky with some of these.

While sitting on a fallen log at the edge of a swamp, waiting for kiwi calls, I heard what I believed to be some rats behind me scurrying through the vegetation. One of the animals came closer and I remained motionless. Suddenly it started sniffing, and in the moonlight I saw a medium-sized kiwi coming straight towards me. It stuck its long ivory-coloured bill into one of my trouser legs, took a few deep sniffs, turned around and calmly went on its way again into the darkness of the forest. This bird was followed on the same track by a smaller juvenile or chick a few minutes later, and a much bigger female a couple of minutes after the juvenile. This incident — my first encounter with a kiwi in the wild — gave us some impressions about the life and habits of these birds. First, kiwis are not naturally aggressive towards human beings, but rather curious and eager to find out what these strange-smelling 'intruders' are in their territory. Second, it was the male bird that came and checked me out, and he did this by relying on his reputed keen sense of smell. Third, kiwis travel in family groups at certain times of the year, presumably when the chicks are still small. Fourth, all three kiwis used the same 'beaten track' to move through the vegetation. These tracks can be found almost anywhere in Waitangi forest and are probably shared with other animals, such as possums.

In order to facilitate easy observation of kiwis in their territory, it would be advantageous to make the birds familiar with the smell of the observer so that they learn not to fear human presence in their area. The fact that captive kiwis are able to recognise individual keepers by smell alone is well known. This gave rise to an idea to scatter around our dirty socks and underwear in one of the territories in the study area, just to let the birds get used to our presence. Those garments must still be lying somewhere in compartment 9, as for various reasons this observation project never got off the ground.

Instead, we opted for catching and banding the kiwis in our study area. In view of the horrific stories of kicking kiwis and sharp claws, and the prolific abundance of fairly tall gorse bushes and dense blackberry shrubbery, we protected ourselves with heavy-duty gloves in those early days of catching. However, later on in the study these implements proved to be unnecessary and even a nuisance. Kiwis are essentially conically shaped, with no other useful extremities to grab hold of but the legs. It is very difficult indeed to take a good hold of a kiwi — they are almost 'slippery' and, owing to their conical shape, they are able to worm themselves out of any situation and certainly out of the gloved hands of a researcher.

We soon found out that the best way to catch a bird is to close your eyes, dive through the gorse bushes on the side of the road, jump distances of three to four metres down the steep slopes and run for the bird that just called. This may sound easy, given a daytime situation, but at night vision is restricted to a very narrow beam of torchlight, which not only serves to scan the immediate environment for obstacles in the course of the fast-moving kiwi catcher, but also plays a vitally important role in detecting the pursued quarry.

Of course the whole pursuit does not take place in silence. Kiwis soon recognise the meaning of the crashing and jumping noise and they can react in two ways: they either 'freeze' and remain absolutely motionless for hours, perfectly blending in with the undergrowth and litter of the nocturnal forest environment, or they move away — and fast! On flat terrain with no obstructions a kiwi can move as fast as a human being, but a moving kiwi is

Brown kiwi, *A. a. mantelli*. Oil, 1981.

Raymond Ching
Auckland 1981

relatively easy to follow because it, too, makes a crashing noise. We were able to pursue fleeing birds for long distances just by following this noise. The chase becomes easier in its final stages, when the kiwi can be seen in the torchlight. However, as the birds have a tendency to change course in an erratic, almost unpredictable zig-zagging manner, there is very little point in diving at the legs in an old-fashioned rugby tackle until the kiwi has actually bumped into an obstacle.

Chasing kiwis downhill is a virtual impossibility. The birds leap and roll head over heels down the slope, thus gaining ground much faster than the pursuer. Chasing uphill is usually far more successful but rather tiring. Sometimes kiwis alternate between running and freezing, which can be extremely frustrating. On a few occasions we observed hiding behaviour that we believe to be indicative of the phylogenetic affiliation between kiwis and their famous African relations, the ostriches: the hiding birds stick their bill and head in a clump of grass and pretend they are invisible!

In some cases co-operation between two kiwi catchers was of value when approaching a feeding bird. Our 'night language' consisted of a simple whistling code and torch signals. In this way a bird could be 'surrounded' and driven into an advantageous area. It was interesting to note how kiwis seemed to be intimately familiar with their territories. When pursued, they usually took off straight into the direction of the area with the most possibilities for hiding, such as bush gullies, swamps or patches with dense bracken and blackberry, where human access or the chance of finding the birds were very limited.

From February 1981 to July 1982 a total of 84 kiwis were banded; 80 of these were inhabitants of our study area. An additional four chicks were caught, but they were too small to band. All banded birds were individually colour-coded with reflective tape, which was stuck over the aluminium serial band. The Scotchlite self-adhesive tape is available in seven different colours and is the same material used for traffic signs and road markings. It lasts for a considerable time in outdoor conditions, even on the legs of digging and soil-scratching kiwis. To increase the possible number of colour combinations, a plastic legband was sometimes used on the other leg. Each colour-banded kiwi was affectionately given a name to enhance the psychological bond between researcher and bird from a human point of view. There may be not much scientific value in having a Tim, Elspeth, Louise, and Jerry running through the forest, but the reflective tape and colour combinations made the birds far more conspicuous during pursuit in torchlight. It also enabled quick recognition of individuals at some distance. Some birds were recaptured or resighted once or twice, others up to 20 times, and some were never caught or seen again after their initial capture.

All captured or recaptured birds were weighed with a spring balance and their bills measured with calipers. The sex of the kiwi was determined by the call it made before or during pursuit. If the bird did not call before capture, its sex could in some cases be established by the length of its bill. Kiwis with bills longer than 11.7 centimetres were considered to be females — which seemed to be a reliable rule of thumb for North Island brown kiwi specimens held at museums. Birds with bills shorter than this could be males or immature females. Breeding males show conspicuous bare patches of skin on their bellies (brood patches that enable the conduction of heat from the incubating bird to the eggs).

Recapture and resighting of the banded birds yielded a massive amount of information on the kiwi population at Waitangi State Forest. Paired birds were found to be faithful to their partner over the one and a half years of research. Moreover, the birds seemed to move about in rather clearly defined areas, territories of about four hectares in size. These two observations, together with our impression that kiwis are intimately familiar with their territories, made us believe that these birds pair for life and remain in their territory for as long as this is possible.

A kiwi survey in 1985 confirmed these impressions. Thirteen of our birds were found again four years later, and twelve of these lived in the same spot as in 1981–82. The other one had shifted more than two kilometres from the location where it was first banded — this young male was only a small juvenile when we first caught it and it did not hold a territory at that time.

Figure 4 shows the accumulated recovery data of some of the banded birds in the northern part of the study area (compartments 6 and 7). Note how the territories sometimes overlap with those of the neighbours. Whether these overlaps are contested areas or simply communal 'no-man's-land' or buffer zones is not clear; they are a little of both. The average distance between the territorial epicentres was about 250 metres, and the territories appear to be evenly spaced.

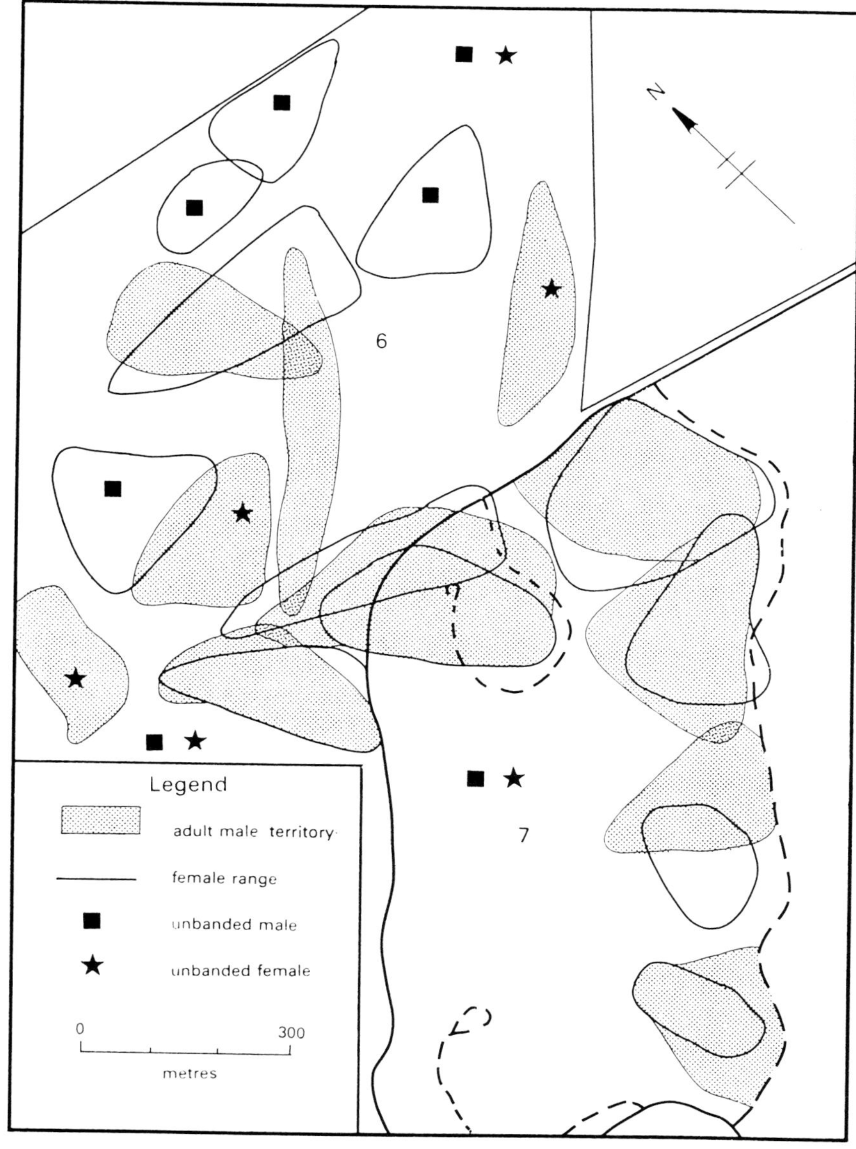

FIGURE 4 Kiwi territories as determined from banding recoveries in compartments 6 and 7 of the study area.

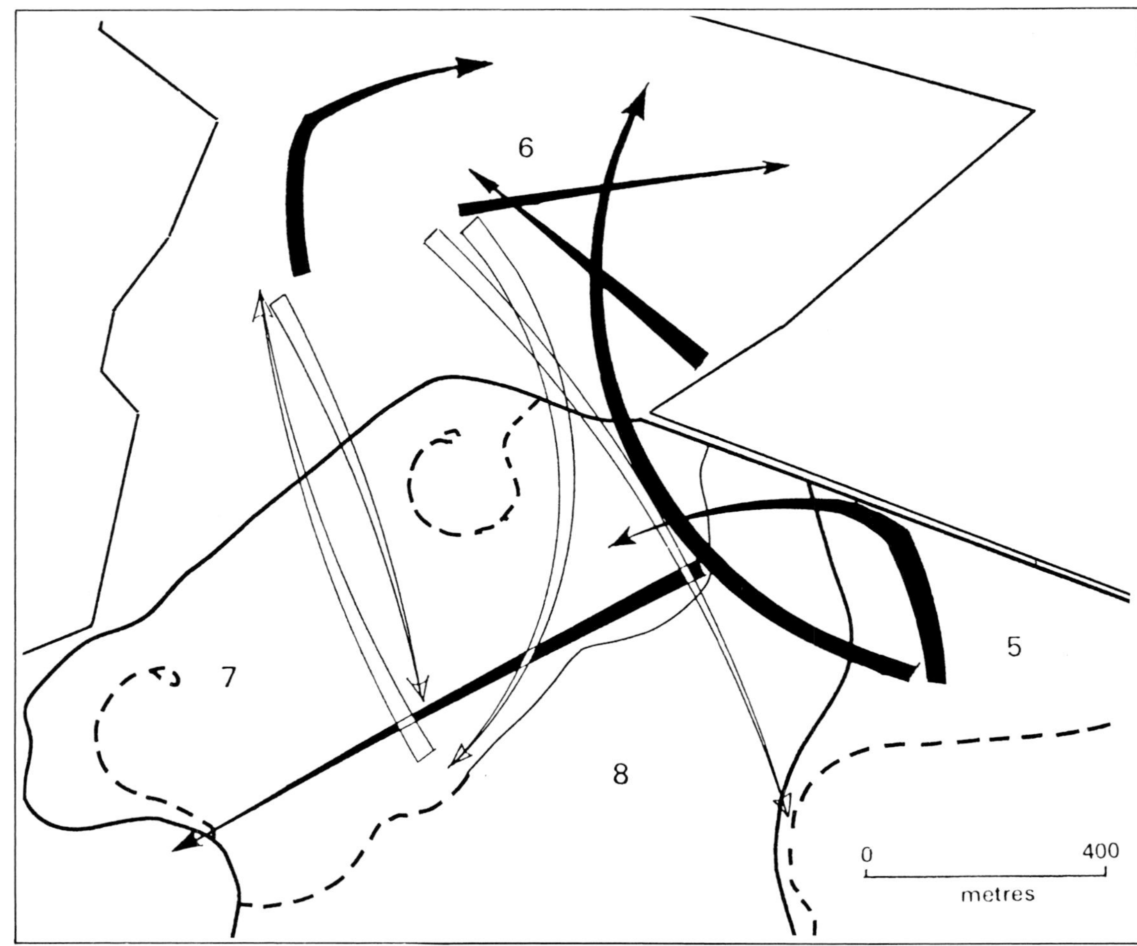

FIGURE 5 Wandering movements of six juveniles (dark arrows) and two adult females in the northern half of the study area.

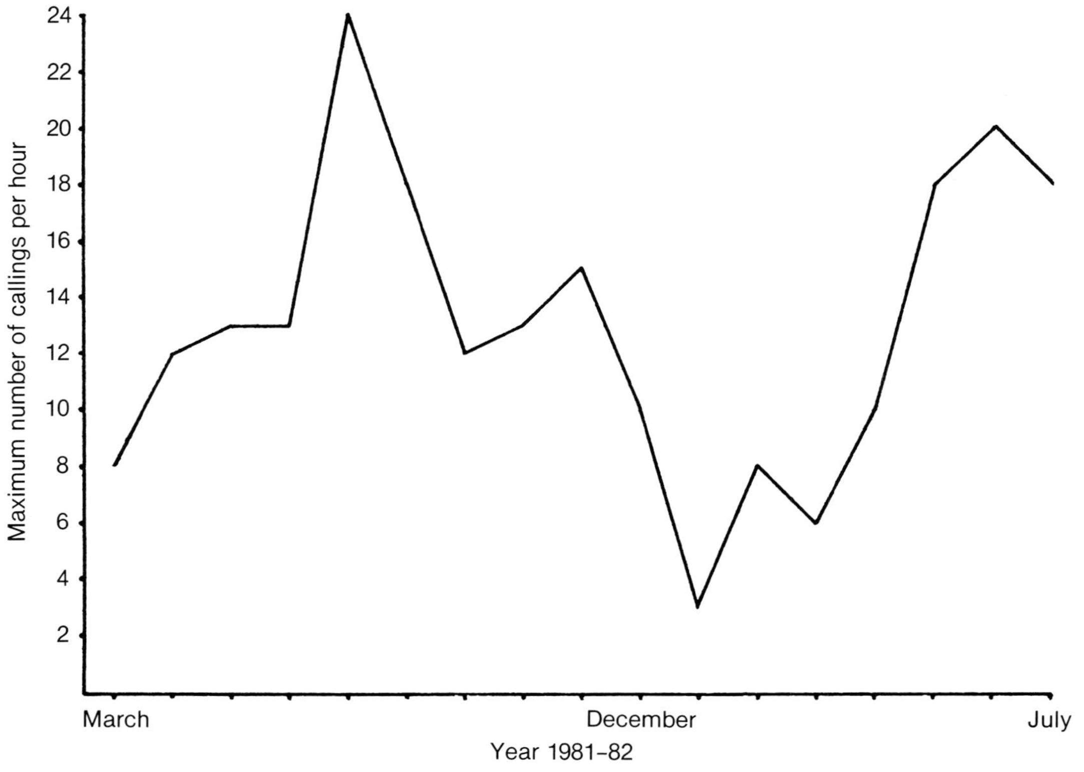

FIGURE 6 Kiwi calling rates in Waitangi State Forest, May 1981 to July 1982.

However, one 'territory' in the centre of compartment 6 seemed unoccupied. This coincided with the presence of a seemingly unpaired female that was found wandering over unusually long distances (up to 1,100 metres). Perhaps an established pair had recently broken up due to the death of the male, and the resident female showed her grief by erratic wandering behaviour. One other unpaired female was recaptured far away from the initial banding site (1,200 metres). We believe that these wandering adult females do not hold a territory. A similar wandering behaviour was found with banded juveniles (Figure 5).

Territoriality is a common phenomenon in the animal kingdom, and kiwis are no exception to this generality. To have a territory and to be intimately familiar with that area is certainly advantageous; kiwis have detailed knowledge of the best feeding, sleeping and shelter sites and, in the breeding season, are able to select the best nesting site. The only bother with a territory is that it has to be proclaimed and defended against intruders and neighbours and other interested parties of the same species. How does the nocturnal, ground-dwelling kiwi, a bird with limited eyesight, actually achieve this? It has no means of visual territorial display, as there is nothing to display with on its dull body. Moreover, the almost blind neighbours 250 metres further up in the pitch-black forest will not be able to see anything anyway. A territorial demarkation by means of aromatic boundary pegs (droppings?) would suit the kiwis with their keen sense of smell, but we found no indication of this. Of course, the birds know their territories by smell, but that is almost certainly a learned experience after tramping through the same area for many years.

The answer lies in the combination of the kiwi's ears and its vocal behaviour. The large ear apertures indicate an acute sense of hearing, and this appears to be correct. Often a kiwi can be seen cocking its head as if it is listening very carefully.

Kiwi calls were monitored during our study and of the 1,032 recorded vocalisations, 75.3 per cent were made by males. Calling frequency peaked conspicuously in the first months of the breeding season (Figure 6). This suggests that it is mainly the male birds who proclaim their territory, and that they get especially wound up during the mating period. Excited vocal display of male kiwis was often heard or observed when a neighbouring male ventured too close to a bird feeding at the edge of its territory. Vocal duels were usually effective in separating quarrelling males. Some amount of 'trespassing' occurred at times, judging from the overlaps in territorial areas as shown in Figure 4, but this only took place when the resident male was feeding at the opposite side of its territory. Females showed a slightly greater overlap than males, probably because they pose less of a threat to the stability of the male's territory.

The importance of vocalisations between neighbouring birds was highlighted when we chased a bird far beyond the boundaries of its territory. The kiwi emitted short bursts of calls that were answered immediately by the resident birds around him. These reply calls were used as beacons and 'guided' the displaced kiwi back to its own territory and mate. It may well be that a kiwi has a stereophonic picture of its home patch relative to its noisy neighbours.

Although vocal duels were usually effective in keeping quarrelling males separate, physical combat did occur. We twice watched, at close quarters, fighting between rival males. In one case, growling and vigorous movements in the undergrowth culminated in a chase, during which the resident male stopped three times to call excitedly. The ejected male ran back to its own territory, from where it called back some minutes later. Here we find the aggressive, territorial side of the kiwi as reported in earlier literature, and there is little doubt that some male kiwis will vigorously defend their area or their nest against unwanted intruders, even human beings.

Females tend to be far more placid than males, and are also easier to catch. Although this could be a reflection of the differences between the sexes (females are larger than males and hence perhaps a bit more sluggish), it seems far more likely that this is caused by the fact that females are not the main defenders of the territory. Territorial behaviour includes aspects of both attack and avoidance, and females do not appear to be very skilled in either of these strategies. Their calls — a series of rather throaty and gargling sounds — are usually muffled through the undergrowth and certainly do not carry as far as the shrill male vocalisations. All these factors indicate that the male is indeed the main proclaimer and defender of the territory of the pair.

Vocal activity usually began about 45 minutes after sunset, although on a few occasions kiwis were heard calling only five minutes after the sun went down. The first calls of the evening were soon labelled 'the waking-up calls', as both males and females seemingly 'talked' to each other when they stretched their legs after a good day's sleep. The vocalisations peaked in the first hour or so after these waking-up calls. Later on in the night, two or three hours after darkness, the calling frequency tended to drop to occasional and irregular bursts of vocal activity, which remained a relatively low-key affair until an hour before dawn, when vocalisations could increase spasmodically.

Kiwi calling rates fluctuated not only nightly and seasonally (a sharp increase during the mating season), but also from night to night. On two consecutive nights with almost identical weather conditions, the number of calls per hour could differ remarkably. Initially it was very difficult to make sense out of this erratic calling behaviour. A direct link with certain weather patterns was not very obvious. On nights with heavy rain or high winds, few kiwis were heard calling, but this could also reflect the observers' inability to hear those calls in the midst of considerable background noise.

Some factors seemed to have a more or less predictable effect on the calling rates. During a bright full moon, kiwis were generally silent, which was a pity — on those nights visibility in the forest is optimal for catching the birds! The absence of kiwi calls, and sometimes even any other kiwi sounds, was quite remarkable, and made us wonder if the birds remained in their burrows. During the period before and after full moon (first and last quarter), kiwis were still not very vocal, although their presence could be detected via feeding sounds. The highest calling rates were generally obtained around the new moon phase on dark but clear nights in autumn and early winter. But then again, on very black nights kiwis could be rather quiet.

For the purpose of a more accurate census of kiwis, it would certainly be helpful to be able to distinguish individual kiwis from each other by their call alone. Unfortunately, without the aid of a sonograph this is impossible. The call of the North Island brown kiwi consists of a series of cries — males utter a shrill, almost whistling sound, and females sound like they are forever scraping their throats. The calls usually last about 30 seconds. Some kiwis can drag on for about a minute or so (up to 42 cries in one call). However, the length of the call was definitely not constant for each individual. Some birds sounded distinctly different — one male in particular added a beautiful vibrato and sang like a little spotted kiwi (*Apteryx owenii*).

When a bird calls, it attains an erect posture by throwing its head upwards. The kiwi holds its beak in a vertical position during a cry and then quickly bows its head in preparation for the next one. On some occasions we saw kiwis stop and call when they were being chased by us, as if asserting themselves. Unfortunately for the poor birds, these vocal duels with chasing researchers tend to culminate in defeat — they get caught!

Observations on captive kiwis showed that juvenile birds do not call until they are about fourteen months (males) and two years (females) old. Indeed, it would be unwise for straggling sub-adult males to call, as this could court trouble from the resident male, the owner and defender of the territory in which the sub-adult might be feeding, even when this territory is the parental one. No doubt the father (or for that matter, any other male kiwi with an established territory) will deal with intruders in kiwi-manly fashion. We once heard a chick that was still under parental care make a calling noise. It sounded somewhat intermediate between a male and a female call and gave the distinct impression of a rather inexperienced vocal artist. These occasional sounds from young chicks may be useful for maintaining the family unit — a means of keeping contact with each other while feeding. How long a chick or juvenile is tolerated in the parental territory is not known, but it seems logical that the juvenile will have to start taking care when the next mating season approaches.

Contact calls between male and female of a kiwi pair are quite common. The waking-up calls usually end up in some form of duetting between the pair. In many cases both birds will call simultaneously early in the evening when they emerge from their burrows. Interestingly, these duets not only take place when both partners emerge from different, widely separated burrows within their territory, but it can also occur when the male and female are very close together.

When studying kiwis, it soon becomes clear that the regular male and female calls are not the only sounds the birds can produce; they have a surprisingly versatile vocabulary. Feeding kiwis make an almost continual sniffling noise, no doubt a result of their efforts to find their prey. These sniffling noises can be heard up to fifteen metres away, and are frequently interrupted by a loud sneezing sound as the bird forcefully expels air to clear the nostrils of mud and dirt.

Nasal grunting is another common kiwi sound. It is usually produced when a pair are feeding close together, and it appears as if this grunting, which is distinctly different from the feeding noises, is a means to maintain contact.

Observations on captive kiwis indicated that mewing and purring sounds were linked to courtship and mating. Indeed, both sounds were only heard in Waitangi State Forest when two birds were very close together and perhaps even in physical contact with each other. Moreover, mewing and purring have been recorded in the period from May to November, with a definite activity peak in June at the height of the mating season. In many cases the mewing transgressed into a loud purring, which was audible from about 50 metres. The first kiwi we caught and banded in our study (a male, captured in the last week of May 1981) drew our attention by making a loud, rhythmical purring sound. It is very hard to describe my surprise and the kiwis' embarrassment when I shone the torchlight over a copulating pair. The ensuing chase ended in the male being roughly tackled and caught — the female got away.

Sounds that we considered to be associated with aggression are bill-snapping, hissing, squealing, and growling. Bill-snapping and, to a lesser extent, growling were heard during boundary quarrels and territorial disputes between males, when they came very close to fighting.

When birds were caught they could produce a wide range of sounds: males tended to express their discomfort, annoyance or fear mainly with bill-snapping and some hissing, whereas females predominantly uttered piglike squeals and guttural growls. These sounds often accompanied kicking and struggling.

The range of noises that kiwis produce and their suggested use as social-contact sounds may give the impression that kiwi pairs or families are very sociable and value frequent contact in one form or another. However, the nocturnal reality of the kiwi researcher's attempts to capture these birds soon changes that impression. It would be very handy indeed if the pair can be caught at the same time, but the male and female are often feeding in different areas within the territory boundaries. The majority of plotted origins of the waking-up calls of a pair also shows that daytime shelter sites (burrows) can be widely spaced and, more often than not, the male and female sleep in different burrows.

To complicate matters for the kiwi catcher, the birds probably change burrows every day. We often saw banded kiwis emerge from their burrows after sunset, but when we returned to these locations the next day or evening, we never found these occupied. The enormous abundance of burrows within a territory allows a kiwi to 'work over' a certain area in its territory and find one or two suitable daytime shelter sites in close proximity at dawn. The distribution of feeding signs (probe holes) and the irregular pattern of change of feeding places indicated that a kiwi would shift from one area to another within its territory. This suggests that the territorial area of a pair is an accumulation of smaller ranges, centred around various burrows.

The extremely complex aspects of the kiwis' vocal and social behaviour, plus the irregularity of calling, makes a census of the population on the basis of observed vocalisations a very difficult exercise. The practical difficulties encountered when two observers attempt to obtain cross-bearings on calling kiwis start with estimating distances at night. Dense vegetation tends to muffle kiwi sounds, whereas certain topographical features, such as valley configurations, will amplify them. On windy nights a strange phenomenon can occur whereby the source of a kiwi call can be misjudged by exactly 180°! This requires a double-check by 'auditory scanning' of the horizon via a 360° turn. The true direction is then quickly revealed. Another problem arises when the two observers are too far apart: two neighbouring birds calling simultaneously can then be plotted as one. We found a distance of 100 to 200 metres between observers ideal, yielding the most accurate cross-bearings.

Interpretation of the obtained data is probably the most difficult aspect of a vocalisation census. When the average territory size is not known, it is hard to judge which calling bird belongs where, especially when the plotted positions have been obtained on successive nights. In other words, deciding whether a calling bird is the same as the one heard the night before only 50 metres further up in the forest is a virtual impossibility, unless the more or less exact boundaries of the territories are known. When Corbett carried out his vocalisation survey in 1978, he arrived at a distribution as shown in Figure 2. When we did our far more intensive listening for calls from March to June 1981, we drew up our distribution map as seen in Figure 3, almost doubling the number of kiwis that Corbett found. By exactly duplicating his 1978 survey technique, we checked the possibility that the kiwi population actually had doubled in three years' time, but the results showed a negligible one per cent difference in number of calling birds. This strongly indicates that no major population changes had occurred, and that the discrepancy between Corbett's data and our own was due to the intensity with which we carried out our vocalisation census.

When we merged the banding data with the vocalisation data, the picture became even more absurd. It became evident that the real number of kiwis

Brown kiwi, *A. a. mantelli*, frightened and distressed. Pencil (detail), 1987.

Apteryx mantelli
Restrained and
distressed. adopt frozen posture.

8.3.87.

Compartment	*Area (ha.)*	*Number of kiwis vocalisation census 1978*	*Number of kiwis intensive vocalisation census 1981*	*Number banded 1981–82*	*Estimated total number*
5	54	10	14	16	37
6	84	1	18	19	30
7	84	12	15	13	26
8	88	18	27	22	36
25	93	4	3	–	–
26	105	28	37	–	–
27 (southern half)	50	18	20	–	–
31 (+ Pukawhau Ecological Reserve)	100	33	40	–	–

TABLE 1
A series of estimates of kiwi numbers in various compartments, Waitangi State Forest, as revealed by vocalisation census methods in 1978 and 1981, and by a banding study in 1981–82.

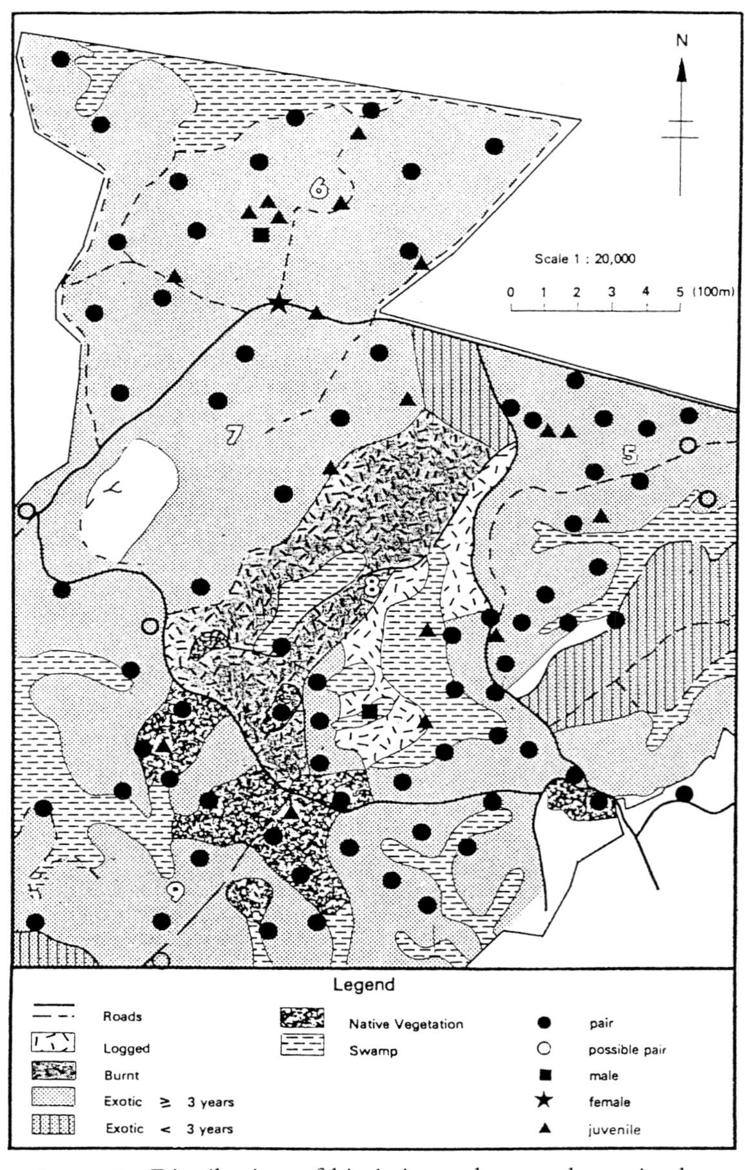

FIGURE 7 Distribution of kiwis in study area determined from vocalisation census and banding recoveries 1981–82.

present far surpassed any estimation that could have been obtained by just listening for calls. Of course, this dawned on us while we were banding kiwis — we kept on finding unbanded birds in areas where we thought we had caught them all! And even towards the end of our research we knew of the existence of many unbanded birds in our study area. Table 1 gives an impression of the continually updated series of estimations of kiwi numbers in our study area from 1978 to 1982. Our final estimate of kiwis and their distribution is shown in Figure 7.

A careful and conservative extrapolation of the population figures in our study area, backed up by quick surveys elsewhere in the forest, gave a total number of about 1,000 kiwis in Waitangi. This would mean an average density of one kiwi per three hectares. When allowances are made for areas that are unsuitable as kiwi habitat (deep swamps, clear-felled, burned, and recently planted compartments), the final population density figure would lie somewhere in the vicinity of one kiwi pair per five hectares.

The value of using calls for census purposes is clearly deficient when targeting for the true member of birds. Detection rates vary from 43 to 60 per cent of the population. Apart from the fact that chicks, juveniles and perhaps sub-adults do not call (or if they do, very infrequently), we also got the disinct impression that some adults (pairs?) do not call very often. As calling rates are correlated with the breeding cycle, the presence of near-silent adults could indicate that not all adult kiwis breed every year. Whatever may be the cause, near-silent adults are an elusive bunch and fall, together with the young birds, into the category that will not be detected during a vocalisation census.

As we saw earlier, exactly duplicated vocalisation surveys could be used to determine major changes of the population densities in one forest over a period of time. Moreover, this method could also allow a rough comparative estimate to be made between different areas within a forest. On this basis we attempted to quickly survey four other Northland forests: Puhipuhi, Glenbervie, Waipoua and Puketi State Forests. By comparing calling rates in these forests with the calling rate in the control area (compartment 6 of Waitangi State Forest) on subsequent nights, we could gain an impression of the relative kiwi population densities.

Puhipuhi and Waipoua had higher calling rates than the control area, Glenbervie had about the same rate, and Puketi had a lower calling rate. These observations and results were supported by the level of feeding sign found in these forests.

Vocalisation data should be interpreted very carefully. When comparing calling rates between two forests, it is important to monitor calls in each forest for several successive nights to get an average calling rate for that forest. This reduces the effects of erratic calling by kiwis on some nights. Obviously, a vocalisation census is best carried out in the season when the calling rates are peaking. For the North Island brown kiwi in Northland this is the autumn–winter period. It would be desirable to obtain much more data, linking kiwi population densities with calling rates, so that calling rate comparisons can be more reliable.

The catching and banding programme in our study not only revealed the intimate details of the kiwis' social, sexual and territorial behaviour, it also allowed us to look at each bird individually and gather data on sizes, weight and moulting patterns as well as parasitic invertebrates that live in and on the birds.

Our data confirmed that the earlier quoted bill length of 11.7 centimetres indeed separates the females from the males reliably. Figure 8 shows a bimodal distribution which separates both adult, fullgrown sexes without overlap. No adult male in the sample had a bill longer than 10.6 centimetres, and the mean bill length for 22 adult males was 9.84 centimetres (range 8.98–10.56). The 40 adult females measured showed a bill length range of 11.70–14.20 centimetres with an average of 13.02.

Figure 9 depicts the bill lengths and growth rates obtained from birds that were caught a number of times. Again we see the clearly defined sexual dimorphism of the adult birds as described above. However, these data also show which of the sub-adult birds (initially of unknown sex) will be males and which will be females. Bill growth appears to be fastest in the first months and decelerates with increasing age until the bill stops growing altogether when adulthood is reached. Via this method we were able to determine the sex of birds we never heard calling and who did not have a bill longer than 11.7 centimetres.

The chick in Figure 9 was first caught at an estimated age of one month (bill length 5.09 centimetres; weight 0.36 kilograms). When it was recaptured 70 days later, its bill had grown 13.2 millimetres, a growth rate of 5.7 millimetres per month. Older juveniles (one to one and a half years old) had an average bill growth rate of 1.5–3.0 millimetres per month. In one case we measured, a male's beak shrank by 0.7 millimetres. As this was a chubby kiwi, carrying its maximum weight in June, we believe that, owing to obesity, the cere had pushed forward over the bill. In view of the fact that bill length is measured from the edge of the cere to the tip of the bill, this one had technically become shorter.

Kiwi weights showed a great deal of overlap between the two sexes (Figure 10). On average, females at Waitangi State Forest were 16.5 per cent heavier than males. The range of weights of 31 adult females was 2.06–3.85 kilograms (mean 2.54) and of fifteen adult males the weight ranged from 1.72 to 2.73 kilograms (mean 2.12). Female kiwis usually look larger than males, but only 16 per cent of the females were consistently heavier than the heaviest male.

When these data are compared with the weights of North Island brown kiwis from other localities in the North Island, it appears as if the Waitangi population consists of a rather heavy mob! In fact, the heaviest recorded member of this subspecies is the 'world champion heavyweight' female on the far right of Figure 10 (3.85 kilograms). I named this placid and easy-to-catch bird Corrie after my mother, although I must confess that I never had the courage to tell her that.

Most measured adults lost weight from late November 1981 to mid-February 1982 (Figure 11). Some birds (Corrie!) lost up to 16 per cent in two months. The most important cause was considered to be the sharp decline in soil penetrability, and hence the accessibility to food, as a result of the drought conditions that summer. All kiwis started to regain their weight immediately after heavy rains fell in mid-February. Only one female, which occupied a territory in an irrigated part of the forest, escaped the famine suffered by the adult kiwis and actually gained weight during that period. Chicks also appeared to be unaffected by the drought, probably because of a different manner of feeding.

Other factors could contribute to the weight loss. In summer most of the permanent soil-dwelling invertebrates, such as worms, migrate to lower, moister soil levels where they will be out of reach for the kiwi. Other important soil-dwelling food species (cicadas, cockchafer beetles, etc.) will emerge from the soil in summer to continue their lifecycle as imagoes. All

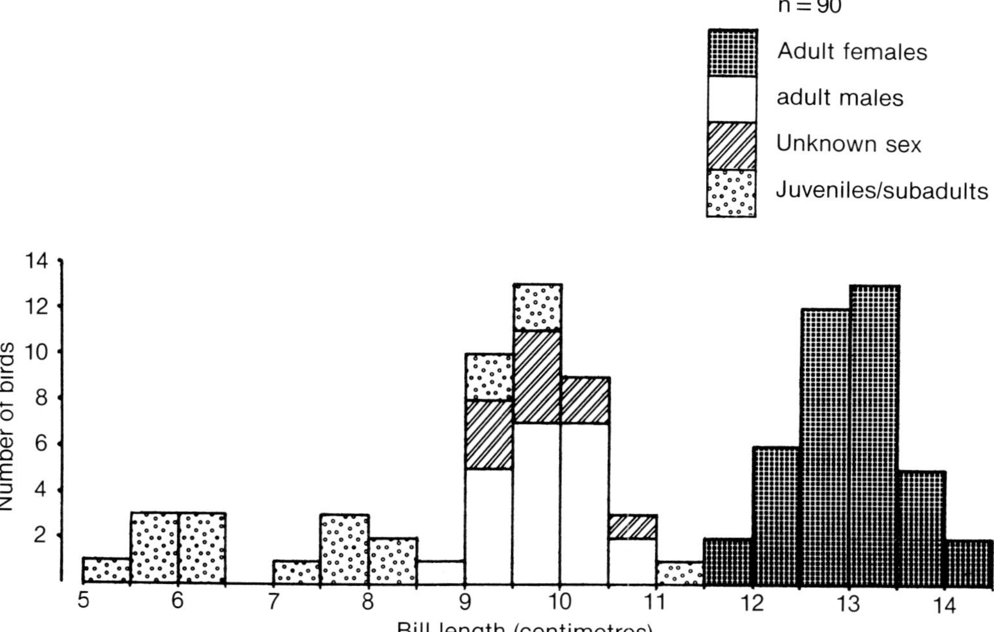

FIGURE 8 Histogram of bill lengths, Waitangi State Forest.

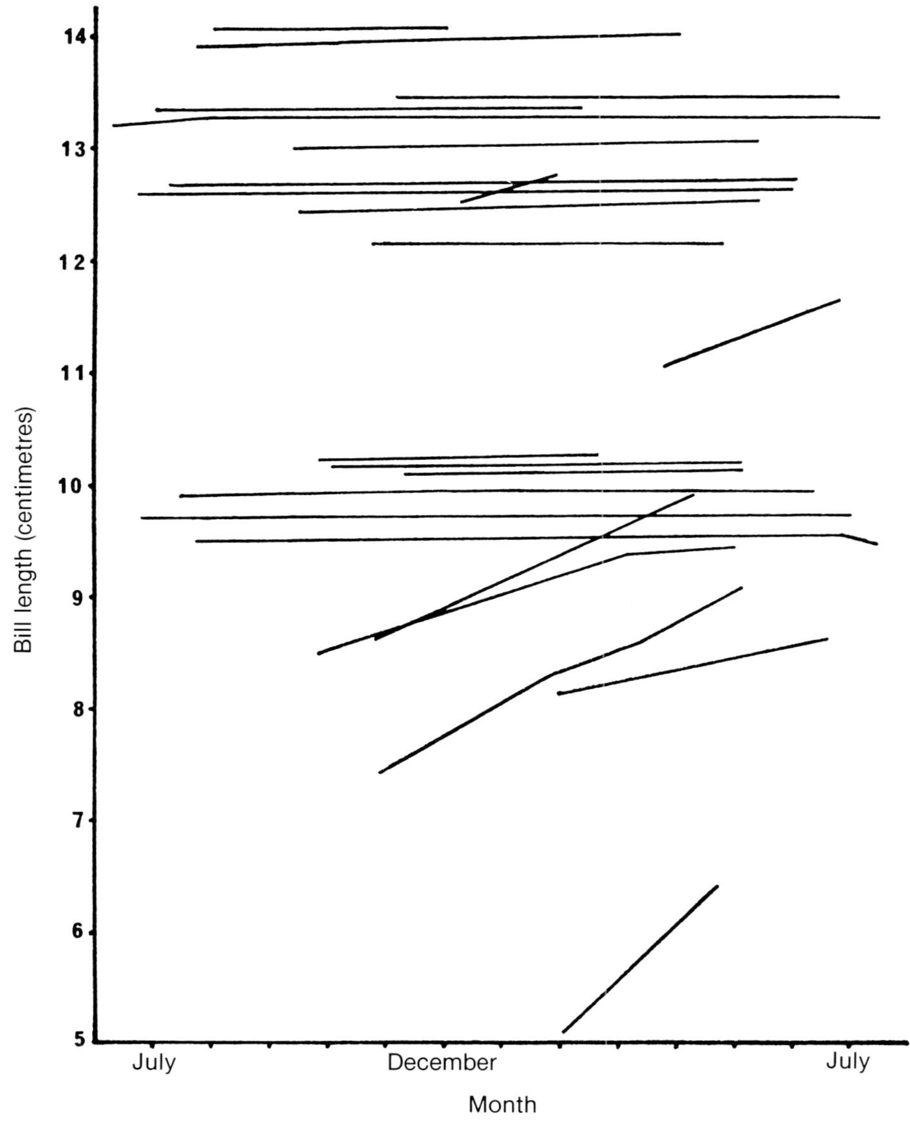

FIGURE 9 Bill lengths and bill growth rates of banded kiwis, Waitangi State Forest, from July 1981 to July 1982.

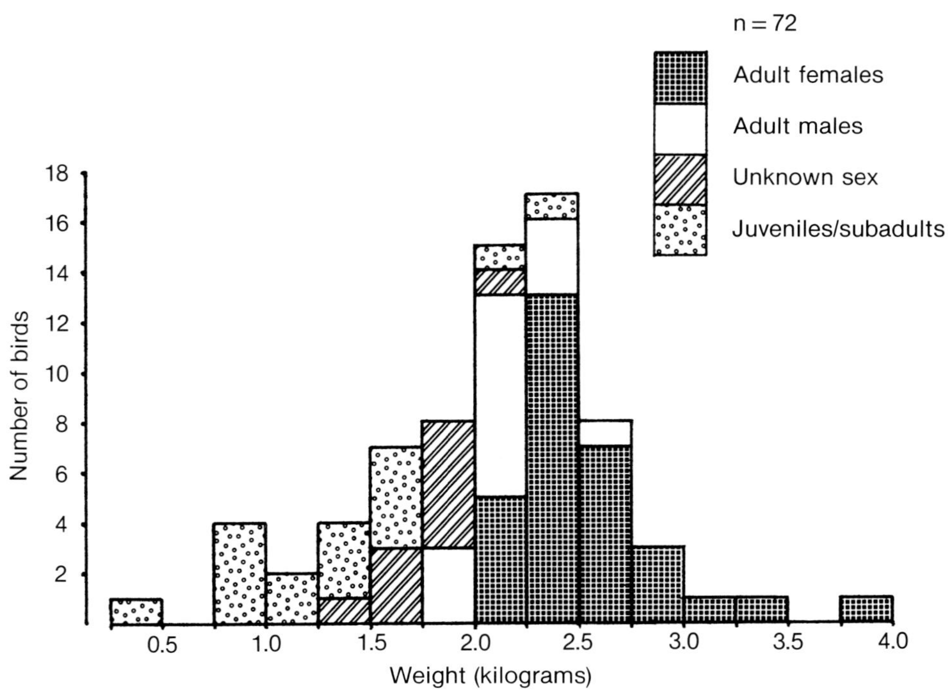

FIGURE 10 Histogram of kiwi weight (weights at first capture), Waitangi State Forest.

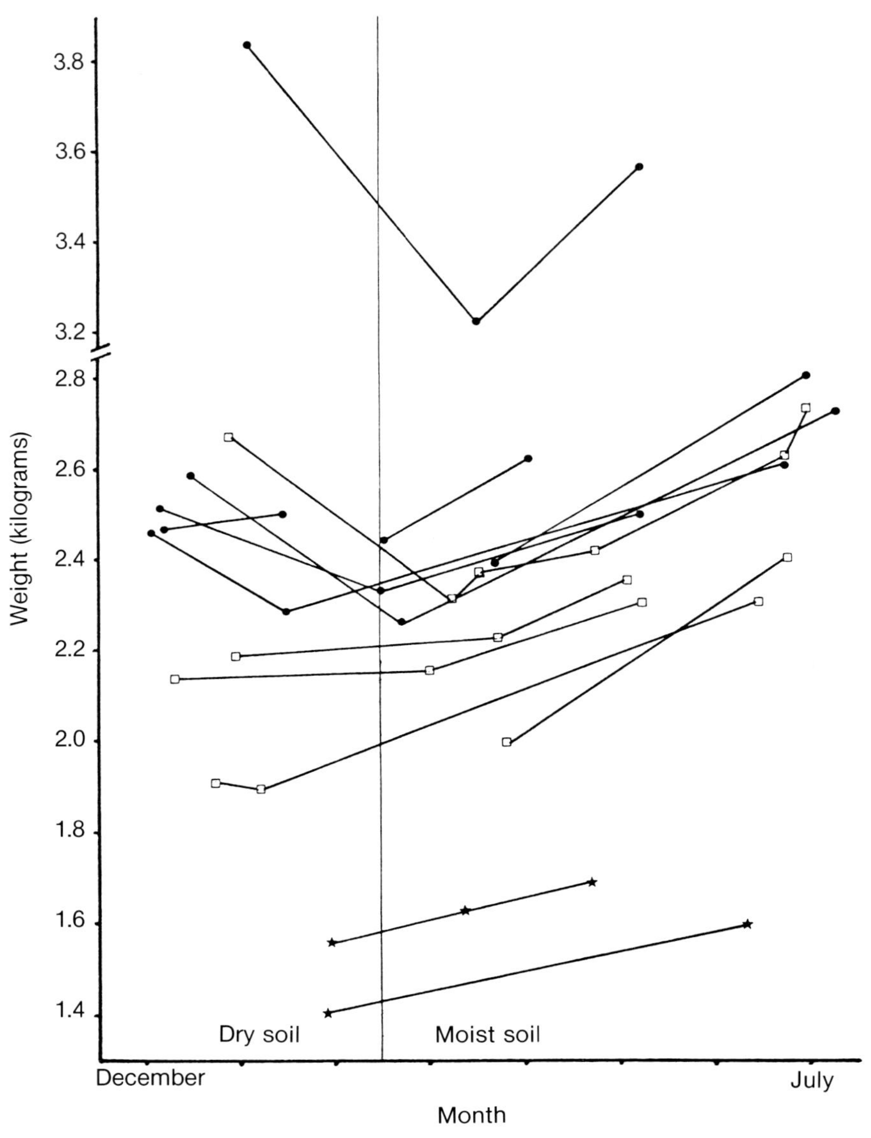

FIGURE 11 Weight changes of banded kiwis, Waitangi State Forest, from December 1981 to July 1982. Females: •, males: □, and juveniles: ★

these factors result in an actual decrease of food available to kiwis. Moreover in Northland the midsummer nights are about five hours shorter than in midwinter, which is a considerable reduction of the available feeding time.

The summer weight loss was not related to breeding. The peak egg-laying period was from July to September, and only one male captured in summer showed evidence of incubation by having a distinct brood patch. Kiwis carry an exceptional amount of subcutaneous fat, which can represent 30 per cent of the body weight. Using this fat, they are reported to survive for three weeks without food. This is rather useful for an incubating male, which can sharply reduce his foraging time without passing out. It is also very useful for females, which have a high energy requirement prior to egg laying. But most of all the importance of large amounts of subcutaneous fat is demonstrated during the long, dry Northland summers.

Compared with the sometimes spectacular examples seen in other kinds of birds, feather moult is a non-event with kiwis. New feathers emerged from the skin in most months without so much as a hint of a moulting season. In midwinter the feathers were somewhat larger than in summer, but that may well be indicative of a better nutrition than a specific moulting season.

Kiwi feathers are of a variable brownish colour with dark streaks, giving the bird an almost shaggy appearance and sometimes resembling a very rough coat of a mammal. After handling a number of kiwis, it soon became annoyingly obvious that this coat consists not only of feathers — fleas, ticks, feather mites and lice are faithful companions of the birds. Every now and then a captured kiwi was de-loused with a household pet insecticide. The bird was dusted with malathion and then placed in a large plastic bag for about ten minutes, with only the head and beak sticking out to prevent irritation of the sensitive nasal membranes. Parasitic invertebrates killed by the insecticide then dropped out of the feathers and ended up in the bottom of the bag. By far the most numerous kiwi pests were feather mites; thousands of specimens were collected. Mites belonging to the genera *Kiwialges* and *Kiwilichus* have been recorded and described from all three kiwi species. The Waitangi kiwi feather mites, however, were found to be two undescribed species of *Kiwialges*. Surprisingly, none of the described species of *Kiwialges* were discovered in the samples. Ticks were also very common, especially around the eyes and beak. They were carefully removed from the skin with forceps. These parasites were identified as the kiwi tick, *Ixodes anatis*, a species that also occurs on native ducks.

Only a few specimens of fleas were collected from the birds via the malathion-dusting method. However, far more elusive fleas were found to inhabit our clothes after handling kiwis. The species was identified as *Pygiopsylla phiola*, which flea authorities consider to be associated with rats rather than with kiwis. Undoubtedly, some cross-contamination could occur here, as rats can enter kiwi nests and shelter sites at night. Host-specific feather lice (*Rallicola* sp.) have also been recorded from the North Island brown kiwi at Waitangi.

During our study no evidence was found of predation of kiwis. Stoats and weasels, feral cats, rats and possums occur in the forest, but they do not seem to bother kiwis much. Cars and roaming dogs appear to be the most significant killers. Some of these road and dog victims were dissected so that stomach contents and intestinal parasites could be studied.

Recent taxonomic work on kiwi endoparasites has added some interesting species to the already long list of nematodes, cestodes and acanthocephalans associated with *Apteryx*. *Toxocara cati*, an ascarid parasitic worm of cats, can be picked up by kiwis via the earthworm, which is an intermediate host. *Toxocara* is believed to be able to develop inside the kiwis, as their body temperature is relatively low for a bird of its size and has been likened to that of a small mammal. *Porrocaecum ensicaudatum*, another ascarid worm, is a natural parasite of blackbirds and thrushes. This species has also been found in kiwis, but only as immatures. It is believed that *Porrocaecum* cannot develop to maturity inside the kiwi because the body temperature of these birds is lower than that of the Turdidae.

The study of the feeding ecology of the North Island brown kiwi population in Waitangi became rather involved, complicated and laborious. Studying the birds' diet via dropping and gizzard analysis was not considered to be exciting enough, so we sampled the forest floor to find out what kind of food items were available to kiwis in the soil, humus, litter layer and decaying logs. Food availability could then be linked up to the actual diet of the kiwi.

Fourteen food-survey transects were established in various parts of the forest, covering pine plantations, native bush, a clear-felled area, and an area that had been burnt off after the trees were harvested. To monitor differences in food availability on ridgetops and in valleys, transects were situated on the hillslopes at right angles with the contour lines — one sample point near the top of the transect, one halfway down, and one point at the bottom of the transects. At each sample point, monthly soil and litter samples were taken at night. As some invertebrate species show daily vertical migration patterns in the soil, our sampling was carried out under the same conditions as encountered by feeding kiwis.

The litter sample size was 50 × 50 centimetres (0.25 square metres) and comprised the total depth of the litter layer, excluding the humus layer. Soil samples measured 20 × 20 centimetres and were taken to a depth of 10 centimetres (4 litres). At each sample point, a pitfall trap was dug into the soil to catch invertebrates that travel over the forest floor. These traps were round plastic containers (diameter 10 centimetres, trapping surface 78.5 square centimetres), half filled with picric acid, which killed and preserved the unfortunate invertebrates.

Data on soil and litter wetness, humus and litter thickness, and soil penetrability were recorded during sampling. All samples were hand-sorted on a large kitchen table, an extremely monotonous exercise which usually took four consecutive days per month.

The invertebrates found in the food-availability survey were preserved in alcohol, identified and weighed. The results of this survey elucidated some important aspects of the feeding ecology of kiwis and gave a good indication of the distribution of invertebrates in the forest.

The erratic distribution of kiwis in the Waitangi State Forest, as revealed by Corbett in 1978, was not related to differences in food supply. Our sampling showed no statistically significant differences in food availability between pine compartments with many kiwis and those with very few kiwis (this research topic was one of our initial work objectives). However, comparisons made between the native bush gullies (and the native forest of Pukawhau Ecological Reserve in the west) and pine plantations showed that the former contain 35 to 95 per cent more soil and litter invertebrates (biomass), than the latter. Moreover, variability in terms of food species for kiwis is far greater in native bush than in pine forests. In the pine forests, kiwis encounter an adequate but monotonous and small range of food invertebrates, whereas a kiwi living in the native bush gullies can feast every night on a scrumptious five-course meal with many side-dishes. This difference in variety of foods was clearly reflected in the dropping analysis.

Another important result from the survey was that soil wetness and soil penetrability are closely correlated. Although this may sound very logical, and is to be expected when considering that Waitangi forest is situated on heavy clay soils, the crucial importance of this correlation for the survival of the kiwi will become clear when all pieces of the feeding ecology finally come together. Soil penetrability was found to be consistently higher in native bush and it also fluctuated less than in pine forests (Figure 12). This means that during the 1981/82 summer drought, the soil and litter conditions were less affected in native bush than in the pine stands. Soil wetness and penetrability were greater at the bottom of the sample transects than on the ridgetops. This was especially noticeable in the pine stands during the drought; the only penetrable soil patches being the swamp margins and partly dried-out swamp arms.

In the clear-felled compartment, soil and litter invertebrate populations declined rapidly in the first six to eight weeks after clear-felling. After a burn-off, the food available to kiwis was severely decimated; usually all that remained of the litter layer of the pine forest were ashes containing no entomological life. In the soil were very few invertebrates, and a six-month sampling programme after the burn-off failed to detect a significant recovery or recolonisation of invertebrate populations, despite a slow regrowth of plant cover.

Apart from all these data on soil conditions and the distribution of invertebrates in forest floors, an excellent reference collection of potential food items was obtained. These preserved invertebrates proved invaluable as comparison material in our efforts to identify food fragments from faeces.

During the food ecology study year a total of 334 kiwi droppings were collected and analysed, 224 (73 per cent) from pine compartments and 90 (27 per cent) from native bush areas. In the first two months (April and May 1981) the number of droppings dissected was only seventeen and ten respectively, but in each of the subsequent ten months, 30 or more were

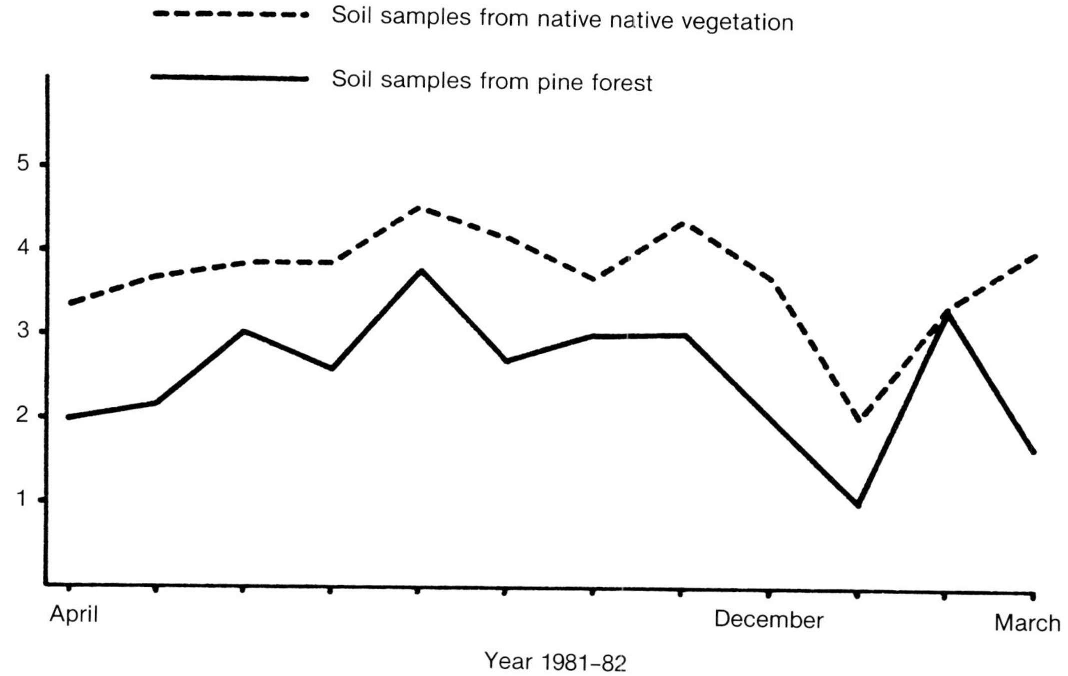

FIGURE 12 Soil penetrability in Waitangi State Forest during the study year. Index: 5 = very high soil penetrability, 1 = very low soil penetrability.

processed. A kiwi scat is easily distinguished from most other faeces encountered in the forest. It may resemble a pheasant dropping, but one sniff will quickly separate the two! Kiwi faeces smell very strongly, and very fresh ones can be detected from many metres away. The scats are easy to find in the rather uniform pine forest litter; in the native bush this is usually much harder.

Faecal material was briefly boiled in a weak sodium carbonate solution to dissolve the mucus content. At that stage the lighter invertebrate remains (wings, small legs, moth scales) could be found floating on the water surface. The residue was sieved through a very fine gauze (size 37 μm) under a hot tap for about five minutes to eliminate fine clay and silt particles. The remaining 'clean' dropping was examined under a stereo microscope. Recognisable fragments of food items were sorted and identified to generic or specific level. This was a task comparable to solving many mixed-up gigantic jig-saw puzzles from which half of the pieces were missing. Soon we learned to recognise striking parts of each food item's anatomy (head parts of beetles, fore tibiae of cicada nymphs, larval mandibles, chelicerae of tunnelweb spiders, etc.) and, with the help of expert entomologists from DSIR's Mount Albert Research Centre, virtually all fragments could be identified.

Annelid chaetae (microscopic bristles from earthworm skins) were also found in droppings, and initially it proved difficult to equate chaetae numbers in scats to number of earthworms eaten. On some worms eight chaetae per segment can be found, whereas on others about 60 chaetae decorate each worm segment. Our soil and litter samples revealed that both groups of worms occurred in the forest in about equal numbers. This enabled us to develop the workable concept of an imaginary 'standard worm', containing 4,000 chaetae, measuring 50 millimetres long, 3.5 millimetres thick, and which has a dry weight of 0.16 grams. Now we could establish the number of earthworms eaten by estimating the number of chaetae in each dropping via subsampling.

A somewhat easier task was the analysis of three gizzards of accidentally killed kiwis from Waitangi. The food remains in the stomachs were only partly digested and the fragments were a great deal bigger. The gizzard contents matched the food-intake patterns found in the faecal analysis, which indicates that we did not miss much when we were sorting through our jig-saw puzzles.

Figures 13 to 17 show the fluctuations of the most common food items in the Waitangi kiwis' diet expressed as average number per dropping for each month in the food-study year. Major food species extracted from the soil are Scarabaeid (cockchafer beetle) larvae, cicada nymphs, annelids (earthworms) and Cicindelid (tiger beetle) larvae (Figure 13). Scarabaeid larvae (mainly *Odontria xanthosticta*, *Stethaspis longicornis*, *Odontria* sp., and *Costelytra brunnea*) were on the menu throughout the year, but mostly from winter until midsummer. Kiwis seem to prefer the larger instars of these juicy grubs, but the smaller ones were also eaten. Cicada nymphs (immatures) are soil-dwellers and spend a number of years in this subterranean habitat, sucking plant juices from roots before emerging from the soil to finalise their life cycle as winged, adult cicadas. Kiwis love these meaty cicada nymphs and eat all instars, but prefer the larger ones. In November, when the full-grown nymphs migrate upwards to the top layers of the soil prior to emergence, their relative abundance is reflected in the kiwis' diet (Figure 13). After November the intake of cicada nymphs decreases as the nymphs emerge, become adults and fly away.

Annelids were not eaten in large numbers in Waitangi State Forest; most droppings had low chaetae counts. This tied in well with the low numbers of

Brown kiwis, *A. a. mantelli*, feeding. Pencil, 1987.

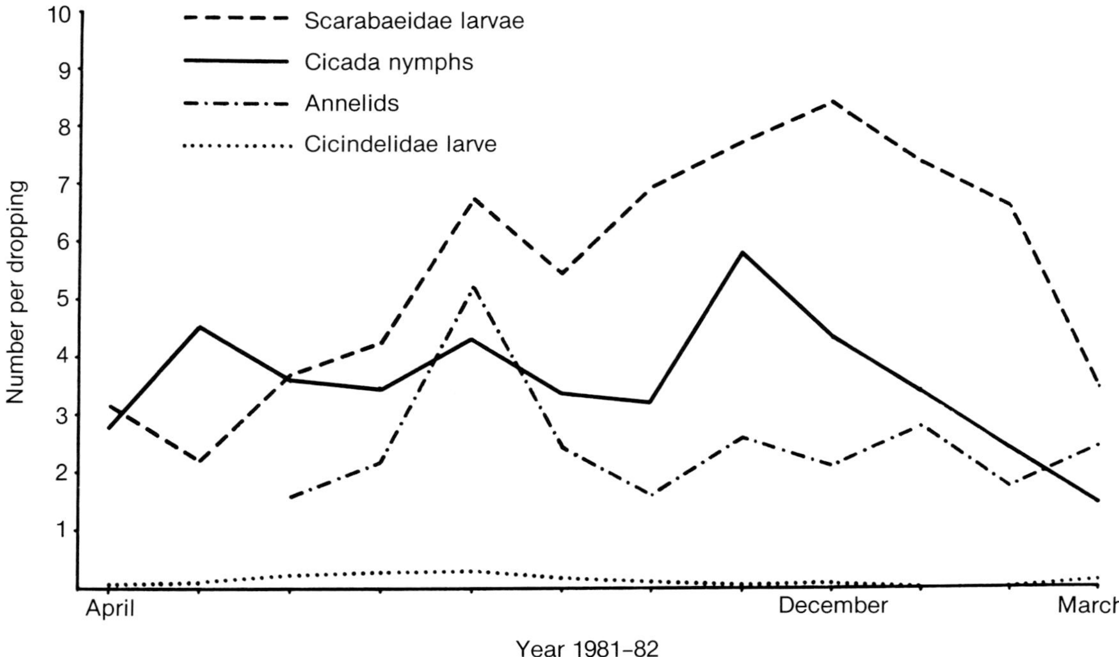

FIGURE 13 Food items originating from the soil and their occurrence in kiwi droppings, Waitangi State Forest.

worms found in pine litter and soil during the invertebrate survey. Earthworm consumption showed a peak in August, which may have been related to the high rainfall in that month and hence the increased soil penetrability. A similar trend was shown with the larvae of Cicindelidae (tiger beetles). These grubs live in small holes or tunnels in exposed clay banks along forest roads. Only in the wettest months are these banks sufficiently penetrable for a kiwi's beak. The conspicuous remains of adult tiger beetles, diurnal, swift-moving Coleoptera, were never found in kiwi droppings.

The main food species associated with litter and humus layers in Waitangi forest are shown in Figure 14. Tipulidae (crane flies) spend their larval stage of life in decomposing organic material. These larvae, also known as leather jackets, often occur in large clusters; once a kiwi detects such a cluster it can feast on a copious meal. Their abundance in October and November was confirmed during the food availability survey. The remains of 45 leather jackets were found in one dropping, and a gizzard contained 310 of these larvae.

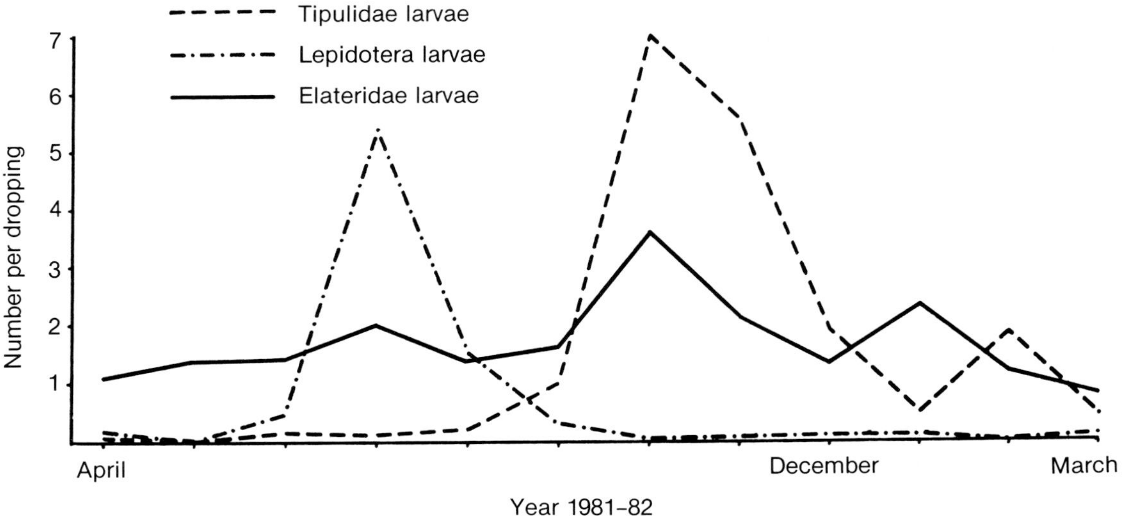

FIGURE 14 Food items originating from the litter and their occurrence in kiwi droppings, Waitangi State Forest.

Lepidoptera larvae (caterpillars) were only found in numbers in the faeces during the winter months, when two small species, *Opogona omoscopa* and *Tingena* sp., were abundant. These caterpillars, like the Tipulidae larvae, also occur in clusters in the litter and feed on decaying organic material. In terms of biomass, Elateridae larvae (wireworms) were the most important litter- and humus-dwelling species eaten by kiwis. The four most common members of this family were *Agrypnus variabilis* (variable wireworm), *Conoderus exsul* (pasture wireworm), *Ctenicera* sp. and *Ochosternus zealandicus*. The latter species is particularly abundant in pine forests and also inhabits rotting logs. Wireworms were on the menu throughout the year in more or less the same quantities.

Other invertebrates that kiwis pick up from the litter and forest floor are spiders, centipedes and millipedes. The tunnelweb spider, *Porrhothele quadrigyna*, a big species that lives in a silk-lined tunnel extending from the litter layer into the soil, was a notable constituent of the bird's diet. Centipedes, which occur in a variety of habitats in and on the forest floor, were eaten throughout the year, mostly from native bush areas. Millipedes, especially *Spirobolella antipodarus*, were common in the litter and logs of the pine forest. This species excretes a strong repugnant smell, which makes it an easily located prey for the kiwi.

Despite the fact that adult Coleoptera (beetles) are a rather crunchy snack, kiwis seem to eat them quite frequently (Figure 15). The three most encountered families in the kiwi diet are Scarabaeidae (cockchafers), Elateridae (click beetles) and Carabidae (predatory ground beetles). The latter family was mainly represented by *Ctenognathus bidens* and *Aulacopodus calathoides*, which were consumed in all seasons. Click beetles, however, were eaten chiefly in spring and summer, and the same four species taken as larvae were also on the menu in adult form.

The yellow-spotted chafer (*Odontria xanthosticta*) was by far the most

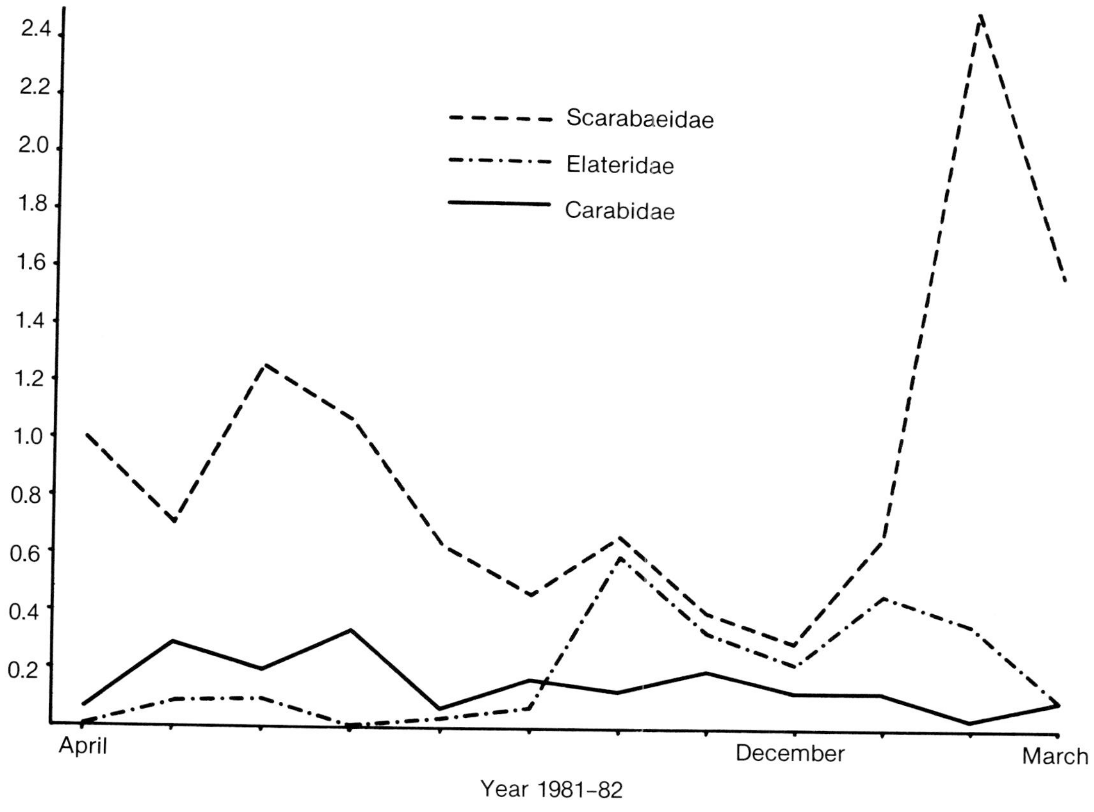

FIGURE 15 Coleoptera adults originating from the litter and forest floor and their occurrence in kiwi droppings, Waitangi State Forest.

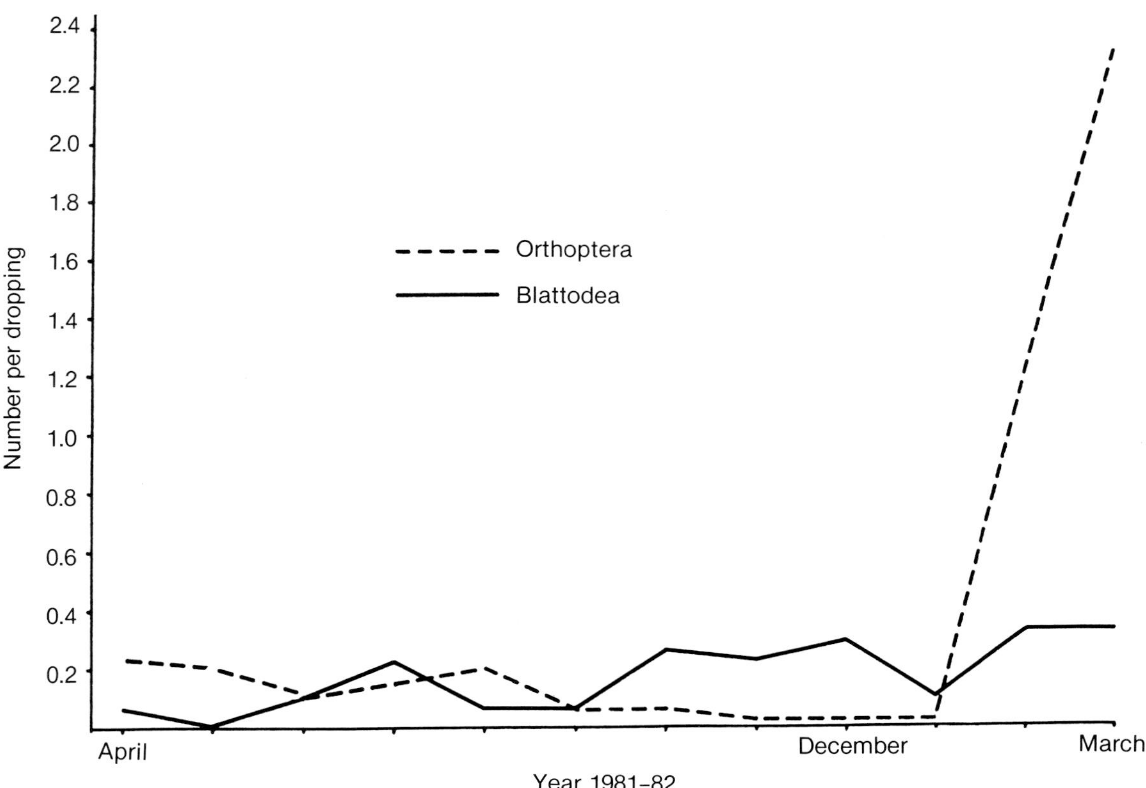

FIGURE 16 Food items originating from the forest floor and their occurrence in kiwi droppings, Waitangi State Forest.

frequently taken beetle in the family Scarabaeidae. Midsummer and midwinter were the peak months for this species in the kiwi diet. This pattern of consumption corresponded very nicely with the annual flight periods of this beetle in Northland. Similarly, fragments of *Costelytra brunnea* and *Stethaspis longicornis* (mumu chafer) in kiwi faeces occurred in the periods when the adults were about.

A rather striking food graph (Figure 16) is the one for Orthoptera (the order of wetas, grasshoppers and crickets). Kiwis consume wetas and grasshoppers throughout the year, be it in low numbers. However, the common tokoriro weta (*Hemideina thoracica*), especially an adult, can be regarded as a substantial snack. The spectacular peak in Orthoptera consumption in February and March was almost totally due to the great abundance of the black field cricket (*Teleogryllus commodus*) in the grassy road verges at that time. The last instar nymphs and adults of these nocturnal crickets develop in midsummer, and populations can reach plague levels after a dry spring and summer. *Teleogryllus* is considered a serious agricultural pasture pest, and 1982 has gone on record as an outbreak year in Northland. Judging from Figure 16, kiwis must have had no problem finding these crickets.

The Blattodea (cockroaches) eaten by kiwis comprised a few forest-dwelling species, but *Platyzosteria novaeseelandiae* (kekerengu) featured most prominently in their diet. These quite large native black cockroaches hide during the day under bark of dead pine trees but come out at night to roam the forest floor. The kekerengu emits an objectionable smell when it gets disturbed, and this will undoubtedly facilitate the hunting kiwi with its keen sense of smell.

The food items depicted in Figure 17 all live in decaying logs and branches on the forest floor. Depending on the state of decomposition of the wood, the insects are more or less available to kiwis, who scratch and rip the logs with their powerful claws. *Uloma tenebrionoides* is a Tenebrionid beetle

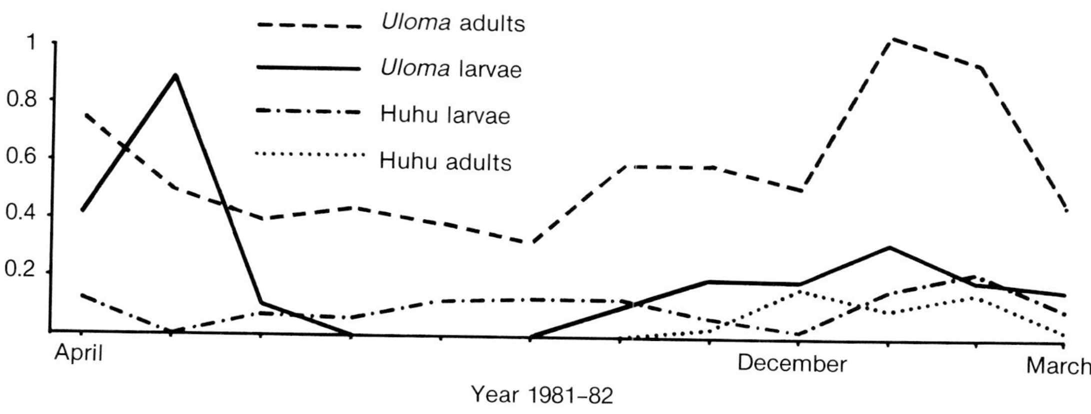

FIGURE 17 Food items originating from rotting logs and their occurrence in kiwi droppings, Waitangi State Forest.

species that completes its entire lifecycle in wood. The larvae and adults inhabit tunnels under the bark. Remains of adult *Uloma* beetles are found in kiwi faeces in all months of the year, but especially in summer. Again, the kiwi should have little trouble finding this prey, as the beetles produce a strong-smelling defence secretion. *Uloma* larvae were absent from the kiwi's diet in midwinter.

Xylophagous huhu grubs (*Prionoplus reticularis*) live deep inside dead logs for two to three years before emerging as adults in spring and summer. The larvae are picked up during the year in low numbers and the adults are eaten as soon as they emerge from the logs. As both the huhu grubs and beetles are large insects, they form a substantial and nutritional food item for the kiwi.

As stated earlier, about one-quarter of all droppings collected came from the native bush or forest, and the bulk (73 per cent) was found in pine plantations. This allowed us to investigate differences in diet between 'native bush kiwis' and 'pine kiwis'. Two examples of such differences are given in Figure 18. Both native bush kiwis and pine kiwis ate Tipulidae larvae (leather jackets), but consumption peaks differed by one month. The reason for this is that the leather jackets from the native bush are a different species from those in the pine forests, and therefore have a different lifecycle and timing of lifecycle. This was confirmed in our litter samples.

The second example of a difference in food intake between the two groups of kiwis is the amount of cicada nymphs consumed: pine kiwis eat more nymphs than the native bush kiwis. The reason is simple: our soil samples clearly showed that these nymphs were significantly more numerous in the soil of the pine plantations. From these two examples, it appears that the kiwi is an opportunistic feeder. Other incidences of increased consumption

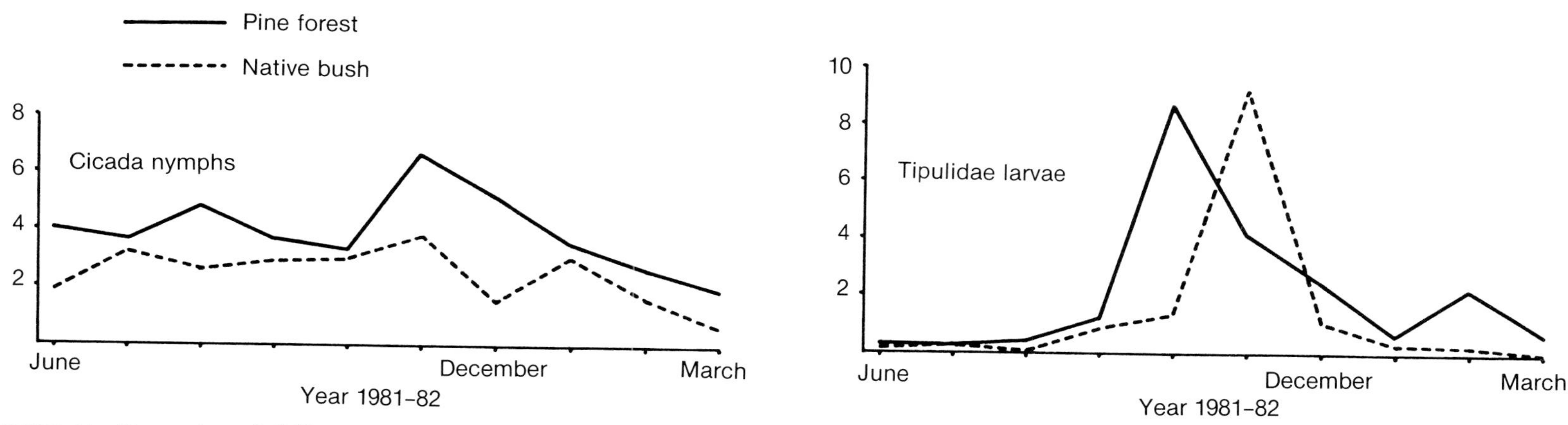

FIGURE 18 Examples of difference in diet between kiwis in pine forest and native bush, Waitangi State Forest.

synchronised with increased population levels of food species seem to confirm this (i.e., Lepidoptera larvae, Coleoptera adults, black field crickets).

So far, the graphs in Figures 13 to 18 have expressed how many specimens of a certain food item were found in a kiwi dropping in a certain month of the year. However, this is merely a numbers game and does not give any indication about the nutritional values of each group of food items. Huhu grubs and beetles are only taken in low numbers, but they are big. Tipulidae larvae and Elateridae are eaten in much higher numbers, but these insects are considerably smaller. In order to make a comparison between the relative nutritional values of each food item to kiwis, all prey species were dried in an oven and weighed. The dry-weight values were incorporated in the monthly results of the faecal analysis to calculate the respective contribution of the various invertebrate taxa to the kiwi's diet.

Table 2 lists the contribution of the most important groups of food items expressed as a percentage of the total dry-weight biomass consumed by kiwis in each month. Owing to the low number of faeces collected in the first two months, April and May, the figures for these months are less reliably interpreted. Moreover, annelid chaetae counts were not recorded in those months. The last column gives the yearly average contribution for each of the food taxa in percentages. Cicada nymphs are the most important food item for the Waitangi kiwi (41.7 per cent), and Scarabaeidae larvae second in importance (20.2 per cent). Note that the reputed kiwi 'bulk food', the earthworm, contributes only 14 per cent to their diet on a yearly average.

As shown in Table 2, the monthly average intake of vegetable matter during the year was erratic and showed no obvious pattern. Much of the vegetable material appears to be ingested accidentally (leaflets, branchlets, pine needles, tree fern scales, etc.), but in some faecal material, high counts of small seeds suggest deliberate ingestion (*Paspalum* sp., *Cyathodes fasciculata*, *Solanum mauritianum*). In the stomach of a bird killed near Rakautao (Northland), we found 114 hard endoderms of toru fruit (*Persoonia toru*). Other authors mention evidence of kiwis feasting on large numbers of berries (with hard kernels) from the native forest, such as tawa (*Beilschmiedia tawa*). Buller assumed that these fruit stones or endoderms act like pebbles and grit, and are useful for grinding food in the stomach. The Rakautao bird certainly supported that

	Apr	*May*	*Jun*	*Jul*	*Aug*	*Sep*	*Oct*	*Nov*	*Dec*	*Jan*	*Feb*	*Mar*	*Yearly Average*
Cicada nymphs	38.6	61.1	52.6	44.1	42.1	44.3	41.2	53.3	43.3	32.5	27.6	19.6	41.7%
Scarabaeidae larvae	14.3	6.6	14.0	16.9	15.6	17.4	21.4	18.8	22.3	30.4	29.1	35.9	20.2%
Annelids	–	–	11.4	14.2	25.8	16.2	10.3	12.1	10.7	13.5	10.1	16.4	14.1%
Vegetation	8.5	0.4	8.7	10.0	4.9	8.7	1.0	1.5	7.0	6.2	3.7	2.2	5.2%
Coleoptera adults	3.8	2.4	3.0	2.8	2.0	1.5	2.3	2.7	8.0	6.4	13.3	6.2	4.5%
Elateridae larvae	2.1	3.3	2.7	4.0	2.1	2.0	5.7	2.8	2.0	3.7	3.1	1.7	2.9%
Araneae	4.3	1.7	3.7	2.3	3.8	5.1	4.4	1.6	2.1	2.2	1.6	2.1	2.9%
Orthoptera	2.5	2.4	1.4	2.0	2.3	0.9	0.9	0.3	0.3	0.3	4.6	10.7	2.4%
Tipulidae larvae	0.1	0	0.2	0.1	0.2	1.2	8.4	4.8	1.7	0.4	2.0	0.5	1.6%
Uloma, Huhu larvae	3.1	1.6	1.5	1.2	1.8	1.8	2.2	1.2	1.0	2.6	3.4	1.9	1.9%
Miscellaneous													2.6%
													100.0%

TABLE 2

Contribution of the most important food items expressed as a percentage of the total dry-weight biomass consumed by kiwis. Waitangi State Forest food study April 1981 to March 1982.

hypothesis: the toru endoderms weighed almost 14 grams and the amount of gizzard stones (1.2 grams) was very low for a kiwi stomach. The average amount of gizzard stones found in the three Waitangi birds examined was 10.7 grams.

When the dry-weight figures from Table 2 are regrouped according to the feeding strata from which the kiwi obtains its yearly average diet, it becomes clear that the birds extract more than three-quarters (78 per cent) of their food from the soil (Table 3). Only 3 per cent of the food is extracted from rotting logs, and 13.8 per cent from the litter and humus layers in the forest. If kiwis obtain most of their nutrition from the soil (cicada nymphs, Scarabaeidae larvae, annelids, and some other invertebrate species), it is obvious that soil conditions are of crucial importance to their well-being.

Strata	%
Logs	3.0
Vegetation	5.2
Forest floor Litter Humus	13.8
Soil	78.0
	100.0

TABLE 3
Contribution of the various forest strata to the yearly average kiwi diet in Waitangi State Forest.

From the end of November 1981 to the middle of February 1982 rainfall in Waitangi State Forest was minimal, which caused a gradual but steady drying-out of litter and soil. In January the soil became rock-hard, especially in the pine plantations (Figure 12). For the kiwi, these drought conditions were bad news. Food became less accessible. Furthermore, we found via our soil samples that in the dry summer months, food species were getting rather scarce. Some groups (e.g., annelids) moved to deeper and moister layers in the soil, whereas others had emerged from the soil as adults (e.g., cicadas).

These hard times resulted in a general weight loss in kiwis, as we saw in Figure 11. It probably also resulted in changed defecation rates, as droppings were rather few and far between and hence difficult to find during the drought. Also, the scats were smaller in external volume but contained relatively more food remains than in other periods of the study year. It seemed as if kiwis retained their foods longer in their intestines so as to maximise its nutritional potential. Analysis of faecal material from the drought months January and February indicated that a large proportion (73 per cent) of the diet was still extracted from the soil. Only the lowest areas in the valleys, such as swamp arms, were easily penetrable, and it became clear that kiwis with territories that included such areas were feeding there most of the time. Evidence for this clever feeding behaviour could be found in the spectacular occurrence of the remains of Scirtidae larvae in the droppings. Scirtidae are beetle larvae associated with swampy habitats, and the food-availability survey showed that these grubs occur there throughout the year. In Figure 19, in which the rainfall in Waitangi and the intake of Scirtidae larvae by kiwis are shown, it is clearly illustrated that swamp-feeding increases in months of low rainfall.

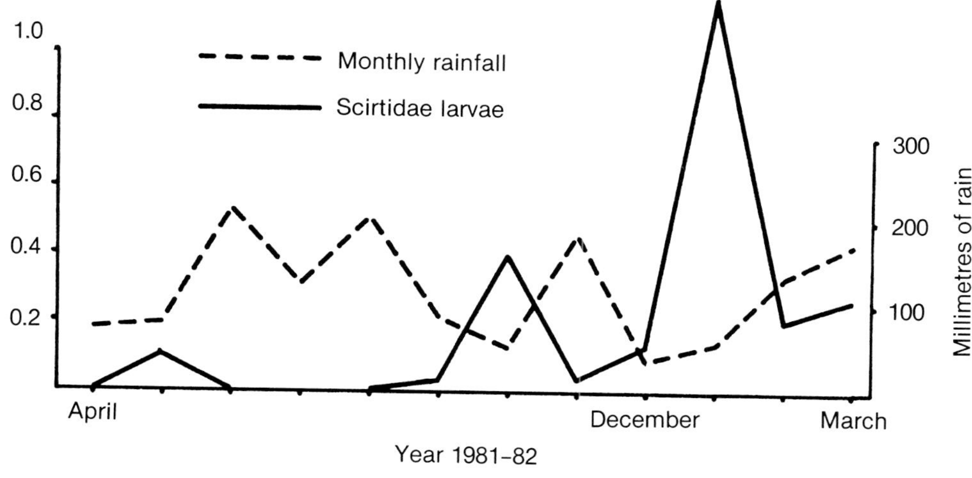

FIGURE 19. Rainfall in Waitangi State Forest during the study year and the consumption by kiwis of Scirtidae (swamp-dwelling Coleopterous larvae).

Kiwis that did not live around or near a swamp tried to ease the famine somewhat by increasing their feeding time along road verges where the black field crickets were in abundance. Others dug deeper into rotting logs and ate some more log-dwelling insects such as *Uloma* adults. The assumption that kiwis are opportunistic feeders became more confirmed when all aspects of the food ecology were put together. The birds will eat any invertebrate food item over 5 millimetres in size when it is available and accessible to them, thereby giving the impression that feeding kiwis are about as selective as a vacuum cleaner.

However, some invertebrates commonly found in Waitangi forest litter and soil were conspicuously absent from the kiwi diet. Amphipoda (sandhoppers) are extremely abundant, yet kiwis do not seem to be able to catch them. A feeding kiwi primarily relies on its well-developed sense of smell to locate prey, but determines the exact location of the food by touching it with the sensitive tip of the beak before devouring it. As soon as a sandhopper is touched or disturbed, it will move fast and in an erratic manner, which greatly enhances their chances to escape the relatively sluggish kiwi. The far more nimble weka (*Gallirallus australis*) is undoubtedly better adapted to capture these hoppers.

The remains of aquatic invertebrates were never found in faeces or gizzards. Although kiwis are capable swimmers, they could be considered ill equipped to forage under water or from the water's surface. Mollusca (slugs and snails) could be common in the forest, especially on wet nights, but fragments were rarely found in droppings; two small snail shells and a set of radular teeth from a small slug species were identified. Because they have no conspicuous internal or external hard parts, slugs do not leave many identifiable remains after passing through the digestive system. Four large, partly digested native slugs were found in the gizzard of a female bird from Rakautao, which suggests that these Mollusca may contribute more to the kiwi's diet than we were able to detect. A similar argument would explain the absence of *Peripatus* from the kiwi's diet in our study, despite the fact that these native evolutionary oddities are present in and under decaying logs in the native bush gullies.

Four kiwi droppings contained bones of the introduced Australian frog *Litoria aurea*. These frogs were very common in the forest, even in the drier parts, away from the swamps. An interesting feature of these four droppings was that most other food items in these scats were virtually undigested and largely intact. This strongly suggests that kiwis end up with a severe bout of diarrhoea after eating these amphibia — frog skins are known to be toxic to some other vertebrates. It appears as if kiwis are fast learners: the low incidence of frog remains in droppings, despite an abundant supply of these animals in the forest, may indicate that frog-eating is a traumatic once-in-a-lifetime experience for the birds.

Earlier kiwi observers recorded incidences of pastoral feeding. Waitangi State Forest is more or less surrounded by extensive pastures with flocks of sheep and some cattle, and it would certainly have been easy for kiwis to stroll into these areas for a feed. During our study we have never found any evidence of kiwis venturing out into the open pastures. No calls were logged from these areas, nor did we find any probe holes. The white-fringed weevil (*Graphognathus leucoloma*), an exclusive pasture-dweller, was a common insect in these paddocks, yet no remains of this weevil were found in any of the kiwi droppings examined.

To compare the possible overlap in diet between kiwis and hedgehogs (*Erinaceus europaeus*) in Waitangi, seven hedgehog droppings were analysed and the food remains identified. In a dropping found near the forest margin at least ten specimens of the white-fringed weevil, as well as 20 black beetle adults and four black field crickets, were identifiable, which shows that hedgehogs will not hesitate to feed from the open pastures. The contents of the other six hedgehog droppings collected from the forest revealed a remarkable diet overlap with kiwis: all invertebrates found in and on top of the litter layer and in humus (e.g., earthworms) are accessible to the hedgehog (and kiwi), and these invertebrates form a major part of the hedgehog's diet. Whether these insectivores are serious competitors for kiwi food is questionable, despite their high numbers in the forest. Hedgehogs hibernate during the cold winter months. Moreover, they are not considered to be able to extract food from the soil, the stratum that supplies the bulk of food items for kiwis.

Some aspects of the food ecology of the Waitangi kiwis relate directly to other important cycles in the bird's life. Their weight loss during the dry summer months (Figure 11) indicates that they are going through a hard time as a direct result of the relative inaccessibility of food. At these times kiwis conserve their energy and go about their business quietly; the calling frequency is at its lowest (Figure 6). With the return of the autumn rains, the soil becomes more penetrable and the birds quickly regain their weight; some even become obese! The times are good.

Small wonder then that this early-winter period is optimally suited to start the breeding season in Waitangi. In the past, some kiwi researchers assumed that there was no distinct breeding season. Captive birds were laying eggs throughout the year, and field ornithologists found nests with eggs in most months of the year. However, captive kiwis are regularly fed on a bountiful meal of oxheart and oats, and sometimes rather surprising foodstuffs such as spaghetti and raisins, which keeps them in good condition all year round. Furthermore, the observation that kiwi eggs can be found in any month of the year is a collective one — it comprises nests from all over New Zealand and also from different subspecies of the brown kiwi.

Some authors suggested that the peak egg-laying period extends from July to February, and this sounds a bit closer to the Waitangi reality. In May and June vocal activity increases dramatically, and the mewing and purring sounds associated with mating behaviour are mostly heard in June and July. Gravid females, especially the ones approaching the laying time, can be easily recognised by their somewhat wobbly locomotion. They walk with their legs wide apart and are a relatively easy quarry for the kiwi catcher. Most were caught in July and August.

The amount of energy a female bird 'invests' in the eggs is enormous. During pregnancy the food intake increases greatly until a few days before laying — then she will fast. Each egg constitutes about one-fifth of the female's body weight, which rates amongst the highest proportions in the world of birds. Usually a second egg is laid some weeks later, and again the female has to eat large amounts of food in order to accomplish that task. The synchronicity of the breeding cycle with food abundance certainly pays off for the female.

Traditionally, a kiwi nest has always been described and pictured as a 'burrow', dug out in the soil, and consisting of a tunnel and a nest chamber. Alternatively a hollow log or cavities excavated under a big tree are the typical kiwi nest-burrow. Indeed, a few of these kind of burrows were found in Waitangi State Forest, but mostly in the native bush gullies. The pine forest kiwis, however, appear to have discovered the 'lazy man's' or 'no-dig' burrow. Toetoe grass (*Cortaderia*) grows in huge clumps, and right in the middle of these dense bushes a kiwi can find comfortable shelter and dry nesting sites. Kiwi nests and daytime shelter sites are also found in dense bracken or gorse, under fallen pine trees covered with pine needles, and sometimes nests are merely a big hole in a patch of very deep pine forest litter.

Eggs were found in the Waitangi forest in the period from July to September, and males with brood patches were caught from August to October and one in January — possibly a late breeder. Newly hatched chicks were found wandering in the forest in September to November. Eggs and eggshells measured from 119.7 × 76.4 millimetres to a sizeable 135.1 × 80.2 millimetres. The latter one is probably the largest North Island brown kiwi egg ever found in the wild. Once the eggs are laid, the female's main task in the reproductive cycle is over. The male will have to carry the candle during the long period of incubation. Captive birds take from 70 to 84 days to complete the brooding. Some birds leave the eggs for a few hours each night to feed, others can sit for many days and nights in a row and keep the eggs consistently warm, and this may explain why there is a fourteen-day range in the incubation period of captive kiwis. Bearing in mind that captive birds do not have to wander very far for this oxheart and oatmeal, the kiwis in the wild will probably be leaving their eggs more frequently and for longer periods of time to feed, causing a higher degree of cooling of the eggs and hence perhaps a slightly longer incubation period.

Males are well equipped to incubate the eggs. They develop large bare patches of skin (brood patches) on the side of the body and on the inner thighs; these enable efficient heat conduction from the body to the developing embryo inside the egg. Furthermore, the incubating birds have built up ample fat reserves that allow them to reduce feeding at night to a minimum — another example of a useful synchronicity between breeding season and optimum food availability.

In the earlier part of the incubation eggs are not turned but later on in the development of the embryo, turning or rolling may happen occasionally — although artificially incubated eggs successfully hatch without being turned at all! Kiwi eggs consist of about 60 per cent of yolk (which is very high when compared with the eggs of other bird species) and 40 per cent albumen. The chick that hatches from such an egg could be expected to be more advanced and developed than the chick of other precocial species, such as ducks and fowl, whose eggs have a yolk content of about 35 to 40 per cent; and indeed it is. The kiwi chick is not just downy on hatching, but fully feathered and apparently ready to brave the elements outside the burrow — were it not for the fact that it carries so much extra yolk in its disproportionately large abdomen that it cannot even get its legs together and has to fast for a couple of days to lose weight before it can actually walk!

Observations on captive kiwis suggest that a chick may stay in the burrow for some six days without food or water, after which it emerges and slowly starts feeding on bits and pieces of twig, small stones (to prepare the crop) and, subsequently, more substantial foods. During the first month of its life a chick may feed at any time during the day or night. After about five weeks they tend to shun the bright light. Whereas chicks of most other precocial bird species are taught and helped to feed by their parents, kiwi chicks emerging from the nest are completely self-supporting and need no parental care. Only one dropping from a young chick was obtained during our study in Waitangi, which is not enough to make sweeping statements about their diet in the first months of their life. The food fragments in that dropping suggested that most of the items were picked up from the litter layer and relatively few from the soil. This is not so surprising, as the bill length of young chicks (about 50 millimetres) would not allow deep probing into the soil. In Waitangi the majority of chicks hatch at a time when litter invertebrates are particularly abundant and some major soil-dwelling food species come to the surface for metamorphosis (e.g., larvae of Tipulidae, Elateridae, and cicada nymphs respectively). Here again we find an example of synchronicity between the breeding season and food availability — this time even in the right strata!

Although most of the juveniles and chicks caught were wandering by themselves, some evidence was found that chicks may keep contact with their parents (or vice versa) during the first four or five months. Several family groups of three birds, including one juvenile, were seen feeding close together, as described earlier in this chapter. This suggests that the offspring are tolerated in the parental territory for quite a long period. However, there must come a time when the testosterone levels (sex hormones) in the father's blood rise, resulting in increased territorial and aggressive behaviour and an inevitable hostility towards the poor juvenile. That is the time for junior to pack his or her bags and leave the familiar parental home range. It seems likely that the parental tolerance remains in place until the next breeding attempt by the kiwi pair. Whether a pair breed every year in Waitangi or sometimes every other year is not known.

When the juveniles had left or had been evicted from their parents' territory, they were found wandering in an almost random fashion. Young males will have to roam and wait until a territorial area becomes vacant, or, alternatively, make a successful challenge and procure a territory before they can start thinking about soliciting for a mate. Although male kiwis can be sexually mature at fourteen months (females at the age of two years) in captivity, it seems likely that males in the rather overcrowded Waitangi State Forest have to wait considerably longer until they can productively express their virility. Dispersal of the kiwi population could be expected to take place via the wandering juveniles. Unfortunately, there are not many suitable habitats to disperse to around Waitangi forest, as it is almost completely surrounded by extensive pastoral areas.

For the kiwi, life in an exotic forest is less of a disadvantage or struggle than the concerned environmental critics initially presumed. Indeed, a pine forest may be a relative 'biological desert' with fewer plant and animal species present, but these forests provide kiwis with all the essentials: enough food throughout the seasons, suitable cover, shelter and nesting sites, as well as relative safety from potential predators. In some of these aspects pine forests offer more to the kiwis than native forests. Daytime shelter sites are everywhere. A simple cavity next to a fallen pine tree which is covered by many years' worth of pine needles provides a dry and dark sleeping place. The kiwi merely has to push its way into these 'burrows' without having to go through elaborate excavations.

Pine forests tend to be relatively free of pigs and cattle. These animals can have quite a destructive effect on kiwi nests and eggs through predation and trampling. Cattle and especially wild pigs are often found in native forests, where their damage is certainly not limited to trampling kiwi nests. In Waitangi State Forest possums are rapidly becoming a nuisance as they increase in numbers. Control of these marsupial pests takes place in the form of poison baits. As kiwis are naturally very inquisitive, it is of paramount importance that the possum baits are placed at levels inaccessible to the birds. This precautionary strategy is endorsed by Waitangi's forest manager. In the past, mortality amongst non-target species, notably kiwis, has occurred in

native forests when baits were carelessly placed at ground level or distributed via aircraft or helicopters.

Some aspects of kiwi life in an exotic forest, however, must surely be rated as a disadvantage or even dangerous when we compare the living conditions of the pine forest kiwis with those encountered by birds inhabiting the more 'traditional' habitat of native forests. Pine forests are managed like a crop, and a number of sylvicultural management practices can drastically change the kiwis' environment. Moreover, the physical hazard of getting squashed by a falling tree or heavy forestry machinery remains a real possibility. A male bird was found incubating two eggs in a compartment that was being logged. Apart from the fact that a tree fell half a metre away from the bird, the kiwi also miraculously escaped being stood on by forestry workers who stacked a pile of freshly cut posts within two metres of the nest. Despite all activity around the nest (including the use of chainsaws within a couple of metres), the incubating male demonstrated a remarkable degree of commitment to his task.

Clear-felling operations turn the forest compartments, and hence the kiwis' habitat, into a bare and messy landscape, without plant cover but with plenty of debris in the form of branches and pine needles scattered over the terrain. In order to facilitate replanting operations for the next production cycle of a pine crop, the debris (slash) is usually cleaned up in the autumn months with a controlled burn-off. These burn-offs constitute a potentially serious threat to any kiwis residing or remaining in such logged compartments. As kiwis are long-lived birds (longevity of captive birds indicates a life span of 20 years or more), and the rotation cycles of *Pinus radiata* forests are rather short (sometimes shorter than the life-span of a kiwi), it seems inevitable that the majority of individual birds in Waitangi will at some stage in their life be faced with the disruptive demolition of their territory.

During our study we monitored the fate of eight banded kiwis in a section of compartment 8, that was to be clear-felled. All birds survived the logging operations and, much to our surprise, remained in their heavily modified territories. At night they were feeding out in the open, amongst the slash of this bizarre environment. We could not determine whether they slept under the piles of slash during the day or commuted from nearby unmodified swamp arms or native bush gullies.

The kiwis remained faithful to their territorial areas for a period up to seven weeks after clear-felling. Removal of forest and plant cover results in a gradual drying-out of the soil and litter layers, owing to the influence of wind and direct sunlight. In the dry and sunny summer months this process is accelerated. As we saw in the food-availability survey, invertebrates become less available and less accessible to kiwis when the soil dries out. This forces the kiwis to vacate their logged territories four to seven weeks after clear-felling.

Gradually the 'logged-out' kiwis established themselves around the swamp margins in the vicinity of their old territory, from where they later dispersed into adjacent pine stands. All clear-felled territories were vacated at the time of the burn-off, so that no kiwis were endangered by this dangerous and destructive sylvicultural practice. After the burn-off, kiwis were only rarely encountered on these barren and black areas — which is no surprise, as the amount of food available to the birds is minimal.

The story of the kiwi in an exotic forest seems to end quite reassuringly: the versatile birds have adapted themselves to life in a pine forest and utilise all the facilities that are available to them. They even manage to circumvent and

Brown kiwi, *A. a. mantelli*. Pencil (detail), 1987.

escape some of the most dangerous and drastic sylvicultural methods, such as clear-felling and burning, and disperse, albeit reluctantly, to neighbouring pine stands. These observations, coupled with the fact that high kiwi population densities occur in other Northland pine forests that have gone through a couple of full production cycles, suggest that forestry practices and kiwis are basically compatible.

However, when we take a look again at Figure 7 it becomes clear that the high kiwi population density to the east and south of the logging and burning area of compartment 8 is due to overcrowding. The birds from the logged territories found shelter in these crowded stands. It is conceivable that these 'logged-out' kiwis had to secure themselves a very small territory in an already saturated forest, and this would have caused some upheaval, especially with the resident birds. Whether the overcrowding has any adverse effects on reproduction or even survival of some adult birds is not known, but is regarded as likely.

Another important aspect of forestry management is the sequence in which compartments are logged and burned. During and after our study in Waitangi State Forest logging activity was concentrated in compartments 5, 6, 7 and 8, right in the middle of our study area. Disruption of kiwi territories on such a massive scale must surely have an adverse effect on large numbers of kiwis that are pushed out of their home patch and have to seek and find a new place to live, only to be moved again a year later by further logging in adjacent stands. Waitangi State Forest's management plan shows the tendency of forming a 'logging wave' which slowly moves westwards — a most unfortunate situation.

The period of time that elapses between clear-felling of a compartment and the burning of the slash is usually two to eight months. Logging takes place from winter to summer and the burn-off in the autumn. As long as there is a sufficient (eight weeks) time gap between clear-felling and burning, kiwis will have vacated the area to be burned. However, in some years the meteorological conditions are unfavourable for burning in autumn, so that certain compartments are left as they are for another year. During that year an astonishing amount of spontaneous revegetation can occur, mainly consisting of gorse, bracken and some native shrubs. Although this results in a far-from-optimal kiwi habitat, some birds recolonise these areas before the postponed burn-off takes place. These birds probably move into those marginally suited areas because of the overcrowding and population pressure from nearby mature pine stands.

The aspects of exotic forestry practices mentioned above will have to be viewed with some concern when kiwi populations are present in a pine forest. For this reason a number of commonsense recommendations have been published which will enable the drafting of exotic forest management plans that ensure the least amount of disturbance to the Apterygid inhabitants and aim at their long-term survival in these forests. Ironically, the North Island brown kiwis appear to be slowly disappearing from most of the original native forest habitats, or at best, maintain their presence in low numbers. The reasons for this are unknown. Only in Northland has this subspecies adapted itself to life in a few exotic forests, where it successfully maintains high population densities despite some disturbing and disruptive sylvicultural practices.

There are some indications that the Northland brown kiwi populations are slightly different from populations elsewhere in the North Island. Their adaptable behaviour is one of these indicators, the relatively large size of the birds and their eggs is another. But the occurrence of two different and new feather mite species in Northland is probably the most convincing indicator of them all. I would gladly leave this matter in the hands of ornithologists who are equipped to sort out these subtle taxonomic differences.

Whatever the taxonomic situation may be, the observations and data obtained in Waitangi State Forest have shed a considerable amount of light on that unique phenomenon called the kiwi. Most of these observations and data will, to a lesser or larger extent, be applicable to brown kiwi populations elsewhere in New Zealand, and perhaps even to the other kiwi species.

BIBLIOGRAPHY

Adams, W. E. 1937. A contribution to the anatomy of the avian heart as seen in the kiwi and the yellow-crested penguin. *Proc. Zool. Soc., London* 107B: 417–41.

Andrews, J. R. H. 1986. *The Southern Ark: Zoological Discovery in New Zealand 1769–1900.* Century Hutchinson, New Zealand.

Anon. 1980. Little spotted kiwi now survives on only two off-shore islands. *Forest & Bird* 13(6): 40–1.

Bang, G. B. 1971. Functional anatomy of the olfactory system in 23 orders of birds. *Acta anatom. suppl.* 79: 1–76.

Bang, G. B. and Cobb, S. 1968. The size of the olfactory bulb in 108 species of birds. *Auk* 85: 55–61.

Bartlett, A. D. 1850. On the genus *Apteryx. Proc. Zool. Soc. London* 1850: 274–6.

Benham, W. B. 1900. The structure of the rostellum in two new species of tapeworm from *Apteryx. Quart. Micros. J.* 43: 83.

Benham, W. B. 1906. The olfactory sense in *Apteryx. Nature* 74: 222–3.

Benham, W. B. 1913. The nomenclature of the birds of New Zealand; being an abstract of Mathews and Iredale's 'reference list'. *Trans. NZ Inst.* 46: 188–204.

Brandon, A. de Bathe, 1889. Inaugural presidential address, Wellington Philosophical Society, 12 June 1889. *Trans. NZ Inst.* 22: 515–19.

Bull, P. C. 1959. Stomach contents of a North Island kiwi (*Apteryx australis mantelli*) from the Raetihi district. *Notornis* 8(5): 143–5.

Bull, P. C. and Falla, R. A. 1951. Observations on birds. In: *New Zealand–American Fiordland Expedition.* DSIR Bull. 103. Government Printer, Wellington.

Buller, W. L. 1868. Essay on the ornithology of New Zealand. *Trans. NZ Inst.* 1. 20 pp.

Buller, W. L. 1870. Further notes on the ornithology of New Zealand. *Trans. NZ Inst.* 3: 37–56.

Buller, W. L. 1873a. Notes on the ornithology of New Zealand. *Trans. NZ Inst.* 6: 112–18.

Buller, W. L. 1873b. Notes by Captain Hutton on Dr. Buller's *Birds of New Zealand*, with the author's replies thereto. *Trans. NZ Inst.* 6: 126–38.

Buller, W. L. 1874. On the ornithology of New Zealand. *Trans. NZ Inst.* 7: 197–211.

Buller, W. L. 1875a. On the occurrence of *Apteryx oweni* at high altitudes in the North Island. *Trans. NZ Inst.* 8: 193–4.

Buller, W. L. 1875b. Remarks on Dr. Finsch's paper on New Zealand ornithology. *Trans. NZ Inst.* 8: 194–6.

Buller, W. L. 1876. On the ornithology of New Zealand. *Trans. NZ Inst.* 9: 327–37.

Buller, W. L. 1877. Further notes on the ornithology of New Zealand. *Trans. NZ Inst.* 10: 201–9.

Buller, W. L. 1882. *Manual of the Birds of New Zealand.* Government Printer, Wellington.

Buller, W. L. 1888. *A History of the Birds of New Zealand.* 2nd ed., Vol. 2. London.

Buller, W. L. 1890. Stewart Island kiwi. (Proceedings). *Trans. NZ Inst.* 23: 602–3.

Buller, W. L. 1891a. Further notes and observations on certain species of New Zealand birds (with exhibits). *Trans. NZ Inst.* 24: 75–91.

Buller, W. L. 1891b. On the large kiwi from Stewart Island (*Apteryx maxima*). *Trans. NZ Inst.* 24: 91–2.

Buller, W. L. 1892a. Notes on New Zealand birds. *Trans. NZ Inst.* 25: 53–63.

Buller, W. L. 1892b. Further notes on the birds of New Zealand. *Trans. NZ Inst.* 25: 63–88.

Buller, W. L. 1894a. Illustrations of Darwinism; or, the avifauna of New Zealand considered in relation to the fundamental law of descent with modification. *Trans. NZ Inst.* 27: 75–104.

Buller, W. L. 1894b. Notes on the ornithology of New Zealand with an exhibition of rare specimens. *Trans. NZ Inst.* 27: 104–26, 650–1.

Buller, W. L. 1895. Notes on New Zealand ornithology with an exhibition of specimens. *Trans. NZ Inst.* 28: 326–85.

Buller, W. L. 1896. Notes on the ornithology of New Zealand. *Trans. NZ Inst.* 29: 179–207.

Buller, W. L. 1898. On the ornithology of New Zealand. *Trans. NZ Inst.* 31: 1–37.

Buller, W. L. 1905. *Supplement to A History of the Birds of New Zealand.* London.

Caithness, T. A. 1971. Sexing kiwis. *Internat. Zoo Yearbook* 11: 206–8. Zool. Soc., London.

Calder, W. A. 1978a. The kiwi. *Sci. American* 239(1): 102–10.

Calder, W. A. 1978b. The kiwi: a case of compensating divergences from allometric predictions. In: Pijper, J. (ed.), *Respiratory Function in Birds, Adult and Embryonic.* Spring-Verlag, Berlin.

Calder, W. A. 1979. The kiwi and egg design: Evolution as a package deal. *BioScience* 29(8): 461–7.

Calder, W. A. and Dawson, T. J. 1978. Resting metabolic rates of ratite birds: the kiwi and the emu. *Comp. Biochem. Physiol.* 60A: 479–81.

Calder, W. A., Parr, C. R. and Carl, D. P. 1978. Energy content of the eggs of the brown kiwi *Apteryx australis*; an extreme in avian evolution. *Comp. Biochem. Physiol.* 60A: 177–9.

Calder, W. A. and Rowe, B. 1977. Body mass changes and energetics of the kiwi's egg cycle. *Notornis* 24(2): 129–35.

Chatin, M. J. 1885. Parasites de l'Apterix. *Comptes Rendus de la Soc. de Biol.*, Paris. 1: 770–1.

Clark, J. D. 1952. Random notes on the kiwi. *Notornis* 4(8): 211.

Clark, W. C. 1983. Nematodes of kiwis. *NZ J. Zool.* 10(1): 129.

Clay, Theresa. 1953. Revisions of the genera of Mallophaga — 1. The *Rallicola*-complex. *Proc. Zool. Soc., London* 123: 563–87.

Clay, Theresa. 1961. A new genus and species of *Menoponidae* (Mallophaga: Insecta) from *Apteryx*. *Ann. Mag. Nat. Hist.* 3: 571–6.

Clay, Theresa. 1972. The species of *Rallicola* parasitic on kiwis. *NZ J. Sci.* 15: 70–6.

Clayton, L. J. 1972. Breeding and behaviour of the kiwi at Sydney Zoo. *Internat. Zoo Yearbook* 12: 134–6. Zool. Soc. London.

Colbourne, Rogan 1981. Why is the kiwi so called? *Notornis* 28(3): 216–17.

Colbourne, Rogan. 1982. Surveys of kiwis in four Northland forests. Unpubl. rep. NZ Forest Service.

Colbourne, Rogan, and Kleinpaste, Ruud. 1983. A banding study of North Island brown kiwis in an exotic forest. *Notornis* 30(2): 109–24.

Colbourne, Rogan, and Kleinpaste, Ruud. 1984. North Island brown kiwi vocalisations and their use in censusing populations. *Notornis* 31(3): 191–201.

Corbett, H., Thode, P., and Reid, B. 1979. A survey of kiwis within an exotic forest. Unpubl. rep. NZ Forest Service.

Cracraft, J. 1974. Phylogeny and evolution of the ratite birds. *Ibis* 116: 494–521.

Craigie, E. H. 1929. The vascularity of the cerebral cortex in a specimen of *Apteryx*. *Anatomical Rec.*, Philadelphia 43: 209–14.

Craigie, E. H. 1930. Studies on the brain of the kiwi. *J. Comparat. Neurol.* Philadelphia 49: 223–357.

Craigie, E. H. 1935. The cerebral hemispheres of the kiwi and the emu. *J. Anat.* London 69: 380–92.

Creswell, R. A. 1959. The distribution of the kiwi in the East Coast region. *Notornis* 8(3): 89.

Davis, P. A. and Greenwell, G. A. 1976. Successful hatching of a North Island brown kiwi at the National Zoo, Washington. *Internat. Zoo Yearbook* 16: 86–8.

De Beer, G. 1964. Phylogeny of the ratites. In: Thomson, A. L. (ed.), *New Dictionary of Birds*, Nelson. London.

Drey, B. 1983. The nesting behaviour of a kiwi. *Notornis* 30(2): 135–6.

Drummond, J. 1907. The Little Barrier bird sanctuary. *Trans. NZ Inst.* 40: 500–6.

Dumbleton, L. J. 1953. The ticks of the New Zealand sub-region. In: *Cape Expedition,* DSIR Bull. 14. Government Printer, Wellington.

Durward, A. 1932. Observations on the cell masses in the cerebral hemisphere of the kiwi. *J. Anat.* London 66: 437–77.

Falla, R. A. 1964. Kiwi. In Thomson, A. L. (ed.), *New Dictionary of Birds*, Nelson. London.

Falla, R. A. 1979. Some aspects of New Zealand birdlife. Sanderson Memorial Lecture. *Forest & Bird* 211: 18–25.

Falla, R. A., Sibson, R. B. and Turbott, E. G. 1979. *The New Guide to the Birds of New Zealand and Outlying Islands.* Collins, Auckland.

Farner, D. S., Chivers, N. and Riney, T. 1956. The body temperatures of the North Island kiwi. *Emu* 56: 199–206.

Fingland, N. and Garrick, D. 1985. Kiwis at risk — brown kiwis and exotic forests. *NZ Tree Grower* 6(2): 36–7.

Finsch, O. 1868. Notes on Mr. Walter Buller's 'Essay on the Ornithology of New Zealand'. *Trans. NZ Inst.* 1: 112–25.

Finsch, O. 1872. Remarks on some birds of New Zealand. *Trans. NZ Inst.* 5: 206–12.

Finsch, O. 1874. Preliminary remarks on some New Zealand birds. *Trans. NZ Inst.* 7: 226–36.

Fleming, C. A. 1986. T. R. Hacket and the Okarito kiwis. *Notornis* 33(4): 245–8.

Forbes, H. O. 1890. On avian remains found under a lava-flow near Timaru, in Canterbury. *Trans. NZ Inst. 23: 366–72.*

Francis, K. E. 1971. The New Zealand Kiwi. Whitcombe and Tombs, Wellington.

Fulton, R. 1907. The disappearance of the New Zealand birds. *Trans. NZ Inst.* 40:485–500.

Gaud, J. and Atyeo, W. T. 1970. Acariens sarcoptiformes plumicoles parasites des Apterygiformes. *Acarologia* 12: 402–14.

Goudswaard, R. 1983. The laying of a brown kiwi egg at the Wellington zoo. *Notornis* 30(3): 252–3.

Gray, G. R. 1844–75. Birds of New Zealand. In: Richardson, J. and Gray, J. E. (eds.), *The zoology of the voyage of H.M.S. Erebus & Terror, under the command of Captain Sir James Clark Ross, during the years 1839 to 1843. Vol. I. Mammalia, Birds.* Janson, London.

Gurr, L. 1952. Some food of the North Island kiwi. (*Apteryx australis*). *Notornis* 4: 209–10.

Haast, J. von. 1874. Researches and excavations carried on in and near the Moa-bone Point Cave, Sumner road, in the year 1872. *Trans. NZ Inst.* 7:54–85.

Haeusler, H. R. 1923. Notes on the habits of the North Island kiwi (*Apteryx mantelli*). *Emu* 22: 175–9.

Hamilton, A. 1878. The district of Okarito, Westland. *Trans. NZ Inst.* 11: 388–91.

Hamilton, A. 1885. A list of the native birds of the Petane district, Hawke's Bay, with notes and observations. *Trans. NZ Inst.* 18: 123–8.

Hamilton, A. 1892. On the fissures and caves at the Castle Rocks, Southland; with a description of the remains of the existing and extinct birds found in them. *Trans. NZ Inst.* 25: 88–106.

Handly, J. W. 1895. Notes on some species of New Zealand birds. *Trans. NZ Inst.* 28: 360–7.

Hansen, R. P. and Czochanska, Z. 1975. The fatty acid composition of the lipids of earthworms. *J. Sci. Fd Agric.* 26(7): 961–71.

Harrison, L. 1915. Mallophaga from *Apteryx*; with a note on the genus *Rallicola*. *Parasitology* 8: 88–100.
Harrison, M. 1970. Kiwi distribution. *Wildlife — A Review* 2: 23–25.
Hartman, L. and Shorland, F. B. 1968. Fatty acid composition of the depot fats and liver lipids of the takahe (*Notornis mantelli*). *NZ J. Sci.* 11: 230–5.
Henry, R. 1895. On Dusky Sound. *Trans. NZ Inst.* 28: 50–54.
Henry, R. 1897. Notes on bird-life in the West Coast Sounds. *Trans. NZ Inst.* 30: 279–93.
Horgan, K. P. 1970. Notes on calling and behaviour of the Stewart Island kiwi. *Notornis* 17(2): 132.
Hunter, J. I. 1923. The forebrain of *Apteryx australis*. *Proc. K. Nederlandse Akad. Wetensch.* 26: 807–24.
Hutton, F. W. 1868. Notes on the birds of the Little Barrier Island. *Trans. NZ Inst.* 1: 160–1, 162.
Hutton, F. W. 1871. *Catalogue of the birds of New Zealand with diagnoses of the species.* Geological Survey of New Zealand, Wellington.
Hutton, F. W. 1872. On the geographical relations of the New Zealand fauna: Birds. *Trans. NZ Inst. 5: 231–9.*
Hutton, F. W. 1873. Notes by Captain Hutton on Dr Buller's Birds of New Zealand, with the author's replies thereto. *Trans. NZ Inst.* 6: 126–38.
Jackson, J. R. 1968. Do kiwis live near streams? *Notornis* 15(4): 227.
Jolly, J. N. 1980. Little spotted kiwi. *Wildlife — A Review* 11: 5–9.
Jolly, J. 1983. Little spotted kiwi research on Kapiti Island: 1980–1982. *Wildlife — A Review* 12: 33–9.
Kingsley, I. R. 1892. Notes on birds. *Trans. NZ Inst.* 25: 107–8.
Kinsky, F. C. 1971. The consistent presence of paired ovaries in the kiwi (*Apteryx*) with some discussion of this condition in other birds. *J. fur Ornithol.* 112: 334–57.
Kirk, T. W. 1895. The displacement of species in New Zealand. *Trans. NZ Inst.* 28: 1–27.
Kleinpaste, Ruud, and Colbourne, Rogan. 1983. Kiwi food study. *NZ J. Ecol.* 6: 143–4.
Krabbe, K. H. 1957. On the unique formation of the brain in an embryo of the kiwi. *Encephale* 52: 612–22.
Krabbe, K. H. 1959. Studies on the brain development of the kiwi. In: *Morphogenesis of the Vertebrate Brain* VIII. Ejnar Munksgaard, Copenhagen.
Larritt, R. D. 1972. Observations on kiwis on Stewart Island. *Notornis* 19(2): 186–7.
Lint, K. C. 1966. Notes on the care and nutrition of Mantell's kiwi at San Diego Zoo. *Internat. Zoo Yearbook* 6: 95–6.
Martin, H. 1885. The protection of native birds. *Trans. NZ Inst.* 18: 112–77.
Maskell, W. M. 1896. On some tick parasites of the kiwi. *Trans. NZ Inst.* 29: 290–3.
McCann, C. 1973. The tongues of kiwis (*Apteryx* spp.). *Notornis* 20(2): 123–7.
McGowan, C. 1979. The hind limb musculature of the brown kiwi, *Apteryx australis mantelli*. *J. Morph.* 160(1).
McGowan, C. 1982. The wing musculature of the brown kiwi *Apteryx australis mantelli* and its bearing on ratite affinities. *J. Zool.* London 97: 173–219.
Mills, J. A. and Williams, G. R. 1978. The status of endangered New Zealand birds. In: *The Status of Endangered Australasian Wildlife.* Roy. Zool. Soc. Sth. Australia.
Morrison, K. 1981. Stoat with kiwi chick. *Notornis* 28(1): 56.
Myers, J. G. and Atkinson, E. 1924. The relation of birds to agriculture in New Zealand. VIII. The pigeons, kiwis, rails, and shore-birds. *NZ J. Agric.* March 1924: 166–8.
Nathusius, W. V. 1871. Ueber die Eischalen von *Aepyornis, Dinornis, Apteryx* und einigen Crypturiden. *Z. Wiss. Zool.* 21: 330–55.
Oliver, W. R. B. 1945. Avian evolution in New Zealand and Australia. *Emu* 45: 55–77, 119–52.
Oliver, W. R. B. 1955. *New Zealand Birds.* A. H. & A. W. Reed, Wellington.
Owen, R. 1841. On the anatomy of the southern apteryx (*A. australis*), I. *Trans. Zool. Soc.* London 2: 257–96.
Owen, R. 1849. On the anatomy of the *Apteryx australis*, II. *Trans. Zool. Soc.* London 3: 277–300.
Owen, R. 1871. On *Dinornis* (Part 16). *Trans. Zool. Soc.* London 7: 381–94.
Owen, R. 1879. *Memoirs on the extinct wingless birds of New Zealand.* Van Voorst, London.
Parham, W. T. 1959. Kiwi near Whakatane. *Notornis* 8(3): 88.
Parker, T. J. 1891a. Observations of the anatomy and development of *Apteryx. Phil. Trans. Roy. Soc.* London 182: 25–134.
Parker, T. J. 1891b. On the history of the kiwi. *NZ J. Sci.* 1(2): 66–8.
Philpott, A. 1913. Notes on the birds of south-western Otago. *Trans. NZ Inst.* 46: 205–12.
Pilgrim, R. L. C. and Palma, R. L. 1982. A list of the chewing lice (Insecta: Mallophaga) from birds in New Zealand. Nat. Mus. NZ Misc. Series No. 6.
Potts, T. H. 1869. On the birds of New Zealand. *Trans. NZ Inst.* 2: 40–78.
Potts, T. H. 1871. Notes on a new species of *Apteryx. Trans. NZ Inst.* 4: 204–5.
Potts, T. H. 1872. On the birds of New Zealand. *Trans. NZ Inst.* 5: 171–205.
Pycroft, A. T. 1898. Birds of the Bay of Islands. Trans. NZ Inst. 31: 141–6.
Rasch, G. and Kayes, P. 1985. The second survey of the brown kiwi in Waitangi State Forest. Unpubl. rep. NZ Forest Service. 48 pp.
Reid, Brian, 1970. Feeding kiwis in captivity. *Wildlife — A Review* 2: 26–30.
Reid, Brian. 1971a. The weight of the kiwi and its egg. *Notornis* 18: 245–9.
Reid, Brian. 1971b. Composition of a kiwi egg. *Notornis* 18: 250–2.
Reid, Brian. 1972a. North Island brown kiwi: (*Apteryx australis mantelli*) measurements and weights of a young chick. *Notornis* 19: 261–77.
Reid, Brian. 1972b. Kiwi eggs laid at Wellington Zoo. *Notornis* 19: 276–7.
Reid, Brian. 1977. The energy value of the yolk reserve in a North Island brown kiwi chick (*Apteryx australis mantelli*). *Notornis* 24(3): 194–5.

Reid, Brian. 1978. The little spotted kiwi — a hunted and destroyed species. *Forest and Bird* 210: 29–32.
Reid, Brian. 1981a. Size discrepancy between eggs of wild and captive brown kiwi (*Apteryx australis mantelli*). *Notornis* 28(4): 281–7.
Reid, Brian. 1981b. A North Island brown kiwi and her egg. *Notornis* 28(4): 287.
Reid, Brian. 1981c. Estimating the fresh weight of the eggs of brown kiwi (*Apteryx australis mantelli*). *Notornis* 28(4): 288–91.
Reid, B., Ordish, R. G. and Harrison, M. 1982. An analysis of the gizzard contents of 50 North Island brown kiwis, *Apteryx australis mantelli*, and notes on feeding observations. *NZ J. Ecol.* 5: 76–85.
Reid, B. and Rowe, B. 1978. Management of kiwis in captivity. Otorohanga Zool. Soc. progress rep. 27 pp.
Reid, B. and Williams, G. R. 1975. The Kiwi. In: Kuschel, G. (ed.), *Biogeography and Ecology in New Zealand*. Junk, The Hague.
Reischek, A. 1884. Notes on New Zealand ornithology. *Trans. NZ Inst.* 17: 187–97.
Reischek, A. 1885. Observations on the habits of New Zealand birds, their usefulness or destructiveness to the country. *Trans. NZ Inst.* 18: 96–104.
Reischek, A. 1886. Description of the Little Barrier or Hauturu Island, the birds which inhabit it, and the locality as a protection to them. *Trans. NZ Inst.* 19: 181–4.
Reischek, A. 1887. Recent explorations north of Chalky Sound, west coast of Otago. *Trans. NZ Inst.* 20: 441.
Reischek, A. 1930. *Yesterdays in Maoriland.* Whitcombe and Tombs, Wellington.
Roach, R. W. 1954. Observations on kiwis; Little Barrier Island. *Tane* 6: 153–64.
Robson, F. D. 1958. *Kiwis in captivity.* Bull. Hawke's Bay Museum, Napier.
Rothschild, L. W. 1893. Note on *Apteryx haasti. Ann. Mag. Nat. Hist.* 11: 43–5, 99, 300.
Rowe, B. E. 1974. Mating behaviour of brown kiwi in captivity. *Notornis* 21(4): 384–5.
Rowe, B. 1978. Incubation temperatures of the North Island brown kiwi (*Apteryx australis mantelli*). *Notornis* 25(3): 213–17.
Scarlett, R. J. 1962a. Sub-fossil bones of the little grey kiwi in the North Island. *Notornis* 10(2): 84–5.
Scarlett, R. J. 1962b. Kiwi courtship. *Notornis* 10(2): 93.
Scarlett, R. J. 1967. Further North Island records of *Apteryx oweni. Notornis* 14(4): 225.
Sharp, R. Bowdler. 1844–75. Birds of New Zealand. In: Richardson, J. and Gray, J. E. (eds.), *The voyage of H.M.S. Erebus & Terror, under command of Captain Sir James Clark Ross, during the years 1839 to 1843. Vol I., Mammalia, Birds.* Janson, London.
Sharp, R. Bowdler. 1888. On *Apteryx bulleri. Trans. NZ Inst.* 21: 224.
Shorland, F. B. and Gass, J. P. 1961. Fatty acid composition of the depot fats of the kiwi. *J. Sci. Food Agric.* 3: 174–7.
Sibley, C. G. and Ahlquist, J. E. 1981. The Phylogeny and Relationships of the Ratite Birds as Indicated by DNA-DNA Hybridization. In: Scudder, G. G. E. and Reveal, J. L. (eds.), *Evolution Today*. Proceedings of the Second International Congress of Systematic and Evolutionary Biology.
Smith, B. L., Poole, W. H. S. and Martinovich, D. 1973. Pneumoconiosis in the captive New Zealand kiwi. *Vet. Path.* 10: 94–101.
Smith, W. W. 1888. On the birds of Lake Brunner district. *Trans. NZ Inst. 21: 205–24.*
Soper, M. F. 1959. Photographing the Stewart Island kiwi. *Notornis* 8(3): 63–4.
Tandan, B. K. 1972. The species of *Apterygon* (Insects: Phthiraptera: Amblycera) parasitic on kiwis (*Apteryx*). *NZ J. Sci.* 15: 52–69.
Travers, W. T. L. 1882. Remarks upon the distribution within the New Zealand zoological sub-region of the birds of the orders *Accipitres*, *Passeres*, *Scansores*, *Collumbae*, *Gallinae*, *Struthiones*, and *Grallae*. *Trans. NZ Inst.* 15: 178–87.
Turbott, E. G. and Wightman, G. C. 1955. A breeding record of the kiwi in North Auckland. *Notornis* 6(5): 150–2.
Tyler, C. and Simkiss, K. 1959. A study of the egg shells of ratite birds. *Proc. Zool. Soc. London* 133: 200–43.
Verheyen, R. 1960. Les kiwis (Apterygiformes) dans les systemes de classification. *Bull. Soc. Roy. Zool. d'Anvers* 15.
Watt, J. C. 1971. The North Island kiwi: a predator of pasture insects. *NZ Entomol.* 5(1): 25–7.
Wenzel, B. M. 1968. Olfactory prowess in the kiwi. *Nature* 220: 1133–4.
Williams, G. R. 1973. Birds. In: Williams, G. R. (ed.), *The Natural History of New Zealand. An Ecological Survey*. pp. 304–33. A. H. & A. W. Reed, Wellington.
Williams, G. R. 1983. Why is the kiwi so called? *Notornis* 30(2): 108.

9

THE AVICULTURE OF THE KIWI

Despite commanding a high profile symbolically in the commercial world, the kiwi survives in its own natural world, unseen and unknown to most New Zealanders and travellers to the country. Even those wishing to seek out the kiwi encounter much difficulty finding this shy, nocturnal oddity in the gloomy rainforests and dense shrublands that are its natural home.

The justification for displaying kiwis in a captive situation can therefore be warranted if for no other reason than simply so that New Zealanders and visitors alike have an opportunity to see and learn of this unique species. In addition to their role at home, kiwis have become wildlife ambassadors for New Zealand and are now being displayed in several of the more prestigious zoological collections of the world, giving millions of visitors access to view the strange flightless bird from the Land of the Long White Cloud.

Owing to its nocturnal habits and unusual characteristics, the kiwi cannot be displayed in the typical avian manner and requires the elaborate construction of a 'nocturnal house'. Government restrictions in New Zealand control the number of kiwis held for display and breeding. The agency charged with the task of protecting kiwis, the Wildlife Service (now absorbed in the Department of Conservation), has maintained a policy of allowing producers, rather than consumers, of wildlife to keep the species. The effect of this policy has meant that zoos and parks with kiwis have spent as much effort in establishing breeding facilities as they have on nocturnal house displays. Attempts to breed kiwis have met with varying degrees of success, but the obvious consequence of such effort has been the gradual unlocking and understanding of kiwi habits and behaviour, formerly not investigated or merely presumed.

The aviculture of the kiwi has, therefore, had at least two differing but equally positive aspects: first, in providing the public access to viewing this species, and, second, in allowing a gradual understanding of the bird to become known from a scientific and wildlife management perspective.

HISTORY

As with many of New Zealand's forest-dwelling birds, the kiwi lacks showy plumage and this, along with its unusual characteristics and nocturnal habits, meant that it was not regarded as a desirable aviary specimen by those Europeans who encountered it last century. Like so many of the freely available birds in the bush at that time, the kiwi was regarded by the Maoris and pioneering Europeans as a useful food source. There are a few accounts of bushmen having kept kiwis for short periods, but in most cases the birds were able to facilitate an early escape by burrowing out of their home-made enclosures.

From just prior to the turn of the last century, a few 'live' kiwis did turn up in Europe and were mostly regarded as curiosity objects — the bird that wasn't a bird. Difficulties encountered in breeding kiwis have since thwarted efforts to preserve what few specimens that did reach zoos, and from earlier in the century right up to the present time, it is a rare and notable occasion when a kiwi is successfully bred outside New Zealand.

The first well-documented account of kiwis being kept and bred on a long term basis in New Zealand comes from F. D. Robson, the then curator of an acclimatisation farm near Napier, who kept North Island brown kiwis from 1932 onwards for a period of up to 20 years. A pair of these kiwis attempted breeding regularly during this time, and notes on breeding behaviour and incubation details were recorded.

Kiwis first appeared on zoo stock sheets at Wellington Zoo in 1912, and Auckland Zoo has had kiwis since 1949, but it was not until the early 1970s, with the advent of the nocturnal house, that the birds could be displayed properly to the public.

By 1972 two New Zealand establishments, Auckland Zoo and Otorohanga Native Bird Park, were both displaying kiwis in nocturnal houses, followed by Wellington Zoo in 1974 and Rainbow Springs, Rotorua, in 1976. Today, there are several other nocturnal kiwi houses throughout New Zealand and more are being planned. Overseas, kiwis are being displayed in zoos in Japan, Singapore, Germany, Holland, England and the United States. The small number of kiwis to be sent overseas in recent times has meant a high demand to use them primarily as display birds, and this has consequently meant a reduction in their chance of ever breeding successfully.

In New Zealand it is more typical for parks and zoos to have outside enclosures for kiwis as well as nocturnal houses, and potential breeding pairs are held in these. There is also the need to supply long-term homes for injured kiwis, as they are regularly brought to kiwi houses by people finding them in the bush. Most have been caught in traps set for the introduced Australian brush-tailed possum, an animal that has reached pest proportions in New Zealand. Kiwis are often injured during land-clearing operations — unfortunately most die unnoticed — and others are occasionally hit on the roads at night. Institutions having a permit to hold kiwis have an obligation to receive these injured birds, because there is nowhere else for them to go, it being beyond the scope of most private people to care for a bird that becomes highly stressed when confined and requires large quantities of live food initially. Many individuals will recover well enough to be released or at least to become a part of the breeding group of the park. It is in fact not uncommon when viewing a kiwi collection to note birds with missing toes, evidence that they were once victims of steel jaw traps.

Otorohanga Kiwi House and Native Bird Park is the only establishment world-wide to have developed primarily for maintaining a captive kiwi colony. The idea for a specialised kiwi park was first mooted by several Otorohanga residents in the late 1960s when they realised that despite the kiwi being New Zealand's national bird, most people knew very little about it and nor, at that time, was it being displayed. The Otorohanga complex now provides two nocturnal displays, a building containing incubator and rearing facilities and ten large outside breeding enclosures.

The National Wildlife Centre near Masterton, whilst not specialising in kiwis, maintains a large number of outdoor enclosures specifically for these

Brown kiwi, *A. a. mantelli*, held for weighing and showing vestigal wing. Pencil, 1981.

[illegible]
[illegible]
[illegible]
[illegible]

[illegible] 8. 81

[illegible]

birds. Only Otorohanga and the National Wildlife Centre have incorporated specimens of all three kiwi species in their collections. In fact, outside these two facilities all other institutions, both in New Zealand and overseas, only hold pairs of the North Island brown kiwi subspecies *Apteryx australis mantelli*. There is one Stewart Island brown kiwi at Orana Park, Christchurch, and at present no South Island brown kiwi in captivity at all.

NOCTURNAL HOUSES

A nocturnal house suitable for kiwis depends on such specifics as correct lighting, ventilation, soundproofing and ground drainage.

Night lighting is provided by evenly distributed mini fluorescent tubes or partially dimmed spotlights. To enable public viewing, the light intensity required is about five times that of full moonlight. The kiwis will tolerate this level of light after being gradually acclimatised to it, but it is interesting to note that even well-adjusted birds are far more active during power failures, when total darkness prevails.

Day lighting of the nocturnal house is a much more expensive proposition, as it requires whole banks of fluorescent tubes. One full-length tube is needed for approximately every square metre of ground space. With newer types of lighting now available, there has been an increasing change to broad-spectrum lights that give out a simulated sunlight. Under this type of light it is possible to grow a wide range of plant life in the enclosure, giving greater aesthetic appeal to the display and a more natural habitat for the birds.

Both lighting systems are wired up to automatic time clocks that meter out the correct night and day lengths, some displays even incorporating dawn and dusk phase-in periods.

Ventilation is the most critical factor in creating a healthy and functional nocturnal house. Inadequate ventilation will quickly lead to a stuffy atmosphere in which birds become lethargic, and fungal growths dominate the enclosure. An over-ventilated room can cause health problems to the birds through chilling. Air-conditioned rooms are often necessary in warmer climates, as kiwis prefer temperatures under 20°C; in New Zealand, which experiences a generally temperate climate, fan-assisted ventilation is regarded as adequate. A variable-speed fan is ideal, as the number of air changes can be adjusted to suit the season, and cool, 'night-time' temperatures can be maintained year round.

Kiwis are sensitive to noise, and as well as the building being soundproofed from external noises, the public viewing gallery must be sealed from the enclosure and sound-deadening materials used wherever possible. Contrary to most expectations, tapping on the viewing window does not induce the kiwi to become more active; usually the opposite happens, and an immobile kiwi is hard to pick out amongst the shadows and plant life of a darkened bush setting.

As already mentioned, a well-designed nocturnal house will grow plants providing the lighting and ventilation are correct. Daily watering is mandatory and a suitable topsoil and well-draining base material are important requirements. The kiwis continuously probe and pad about the enclosure, and replacement of the top layer of soil on a periodic basis is necessary. Most New Zealand parks provide freshly raked bush litter for this purpose, as, apart from natural and aesthetic qualities, this provides much desired invertebrate life for the birds to procure.

The New Zealand Wildlife Service has a set of requirements built into the authority to hold kiwis that relate to the design of the nocturnal house and

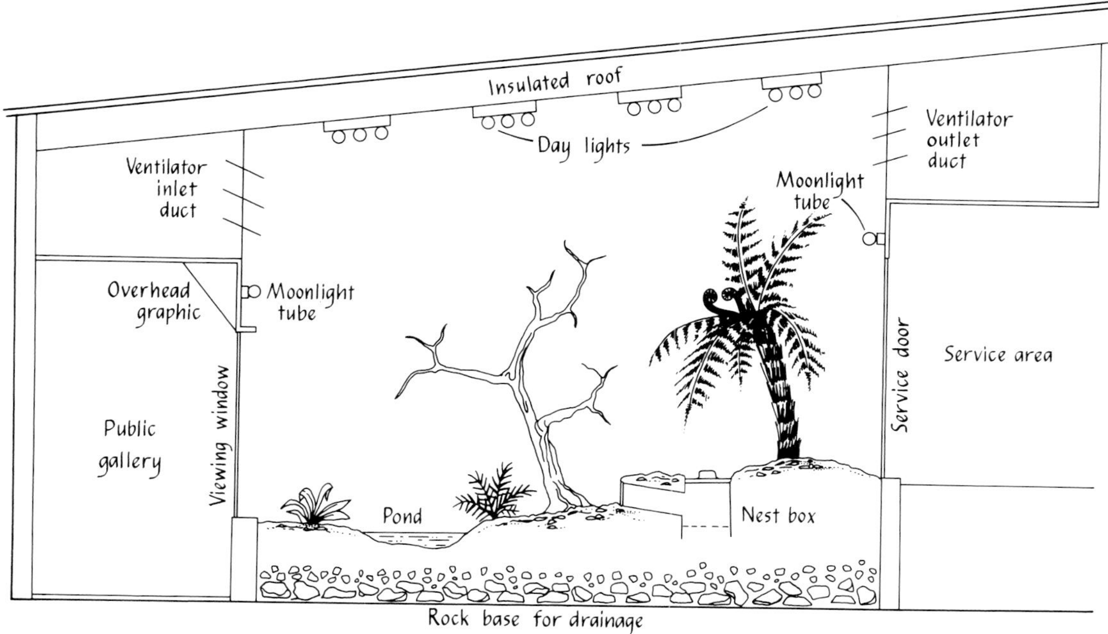

Cross-section of a typical nocturnal house.

ensure good standards are met; amongst these is a minimum floor area of 50 square metres for each pair of birds. Normally only one pair of kiwis is kept in an enclosure, as the territorial and pugnacious nature of the species does not allow otherwise. Many displays do, however, manage to combine other species compatible with the kiwi to add variety. These are typically some species of owl; in New Zealand the only native owl is the morepork, *Ninox novaeseelandiae*, a relatively small species that exhibits no aggression towards the kiwi and epitomises the bush scene with its oft-repeated calls.

The shape and style of each nocturnal house is quite variable within the previously mentioned constraints, and architects have produced domes, 'U-shapes' and other unconventional designs. One consideration that should be taken into account in the planning of a nocturnal house for kiwis is the activity span of the bird and its relationship to public display. Studies on Otorohanga's kiwis have revealed that they are seldom active for more than four hours at a time, often less if they have eaten their fill and no longer need to forage actively. It is the practice of most kiwi displays to lock the bird out of their burrows during display hours, otherwise they may not always remain visible. Whilst this is not unduly upsetting in the short term, it could quite obviously place stress on a bird wishing to retire to its burrow after a normal four-hour active period. When denied its burrow, the kiwi will simply crouch motionless in a dark corner or behind a log, hidden from view, unlike the majority of birds, who retire to a perch and remain visible. Otorohanga overcame this problem to the benefit of birds and visitors alike by incorporating two nocturnal displays into their design. The first is open for three and a half hours in the morning, and the second for the equivalent time in the afternoon, each display featuring a different pair of birds.

BREEDING ENCLOSURES

Outdoor enclosures for kiwis require less detail in their construction than nocturnal houses, with a maximum amount of space being of greatest importance to allow a high degree of natural foraging and burrowing to occur. Kiwis will quickly destroy the ground vegetation of a small area through constant intensive use. The walls of the enclosure need to be buried to a depth of about one metre, to prevent birds burrowing out. They should also

A kiwi breeding enclosure at Otorohanga; note heavy groundcover, vermin-proofing of perimeter fence and large dome aviary in background.

be of a solid material to a height of at least one metre above ground, kiwis can damage their bills on wire and, if kept in adjoining pens, will fight through netting. In New Zealand, owing to introduced predators such as cats, mustelids and rodents, it is necessary to provide vermin proofing along the top of the enclosure walls in the form of an electric fence, metal flashing or a completely wired-over roof. The latter method also has the advantage of keeping out 'free-loading' birds who would otherwise steal the kiwis' food if it is placed out before nightfall.

In both indoor and outdoor situations it is most important to provide kiwis with nesting boxes closely duplicating their natural burrows. Kiwis will normally attempt to dig their own burrows, but if the soil type is unsuitable or the area is prone to flash flooding, the artificially constructed burrow is often the safest resort. Comprehensive planting plus plenty of leaf litter, rotting logs and a small pond (kiwis occasionally require water) are the other basic necessities.

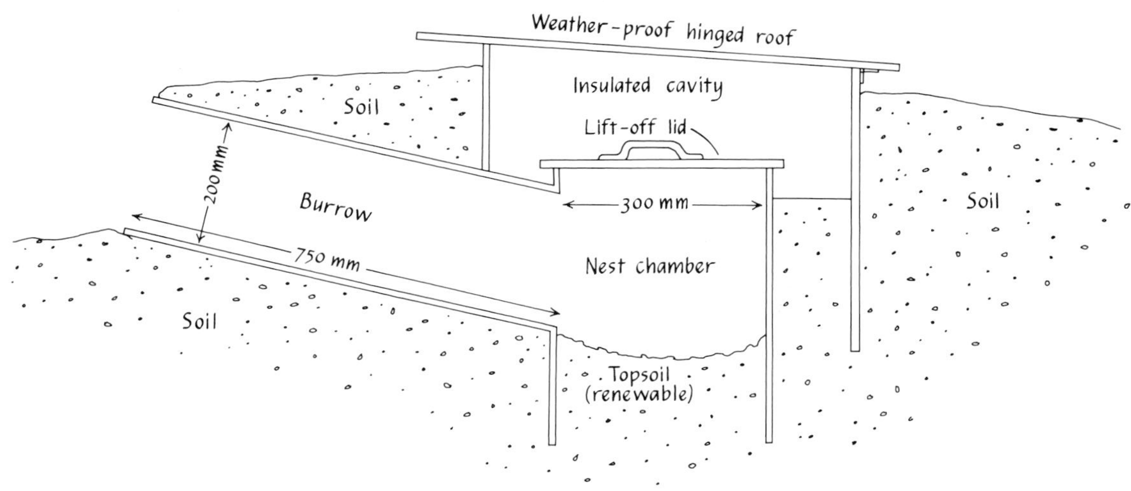

Cross-section of a typical kiwi nesting box, constructed in ground-treated pine and plywood.

BREEDING

The successful aviculture of any species relies on a good understanding of its breeding requirements. Much of our recent knowledge of the kiwi's reproductive physiology has been gleaned through observation of birds held in captivity. However, recent field study research may throw new light on some aspects of the breeding biology. The requirements relating to successful breeding, in theory at least, are relatively few. A pair require their own enclosure with a minimum of interference, an abundant food source and suitable ground to burrow in. In practice, however, the long-drawn-out incubation period produces failures every step of the way.

It is known that kiwis form pair bonds and are aggressive towards intruding birds. In a captive situation it is therefore imperative that once a compatible pair are acquired, they are kept separate from others of their kind. Pairs in adjoining enclosures should be divided by use of a solid wall to prevent fights that could otherwise occur through wire netting. It is also possible that vocal activity from other kiwis in close vicinity may suppress the breeding performance of less-dominant pairs. In captivity, breeding can occur all year round (distinct seasons have been found in the wild) and does not appear to be triggered by light or temperature; the peak laying months are between July and February, midwinter to late summer in New Zealand.

Although kiwis keep growing until their sixth year, birds as young as a two-year-old female and a fourteen-month-old male have been recorded as capable of breeding at Otorohanga. It is normal for only one or two eggs to be laid in a season, and six appears to be the highest number on record for a twelve-month period. If more than one egg is laid, ovulation occurs alternately between both ovaries, two functional ovaries being an excessively rare condition in the avian world. The period between successive egg-layings is about 24–30 days, but has been recorded at as little as eleven days. Copulations occur from about three weeks before the first egg is laid and are repeated several times a day thereafter. As kiwis lack useful wings for stabilising during the act of copulation, the male grasps the female's back feathers to balance himself.

Little in the way of true courtship behaviour has been recorded, it being of doubtful value to such a short-sighted bird. The male will pursue the female, making low-pitched grunting noises, but if the female is not receptive, she will respond by physically resisting her smaller mate and may even lash out or push him aside. Sometimes activity described as 'high spirits' has been observed, more often attributed to the male. The bird suddenly begins leaping about the enclosure at high speed, back-flipping and rolling about in a reckless manner. No real explanation for this behaviour has come to light and it appears to be peculiar to kiwis.

In the month prior to egg-laying, both birds are industrious in their burrow-digging activities. In captivity it is not common for the female to lay in the most well-used burrow, and the pair are more likely to excavate a new burrow, or clean out another less-used one. Fresh material, such as dead grass and leaves, is dragged into the burrow to form a crude nest and is often used to disguise the entrance to the burrow. A definite plug of material may completely obscure the entrance way and is pulled in place while the birds are in occupation. Feathers, plucked by the male in developing a bare (brood) patch on his belly, are used to line the nest.

Female kiwis require a greater intake of food during the early stage of the 24-day egg cycle. In the last two days before laying, the female fasts and can quite often be seen wandering about in daylight, legs splayed apart by the pressure of the huge egg, now weighing between one-fifth and one-quarter of her own bodyweight.

Females have been known to drink at this time and also to stand in water, perhaps relieving the stress on their distended bellies. The energy invested in the egg by a female kiwi is the highest of any bird in proportion to its size, as well as being the largest egg in proportion to bird bodyweight. The keeper can actually feel the egg within ten days or so prior to laying, although it is risky to handle or disturb in this condition, as the egg contents can easily be ruptured.

After laying, the female will often occupy the nest burrow for a day or so, but thereafter has little to do with the incubation or protection of the egg, being more concerned with feeding to build up her depleted fat reserves. The male will have begun incubation within a week of the egg being laid, when his brood patch is prepared, and from then on he will leave the nest only for short periods to feed.

Some males have been known to fast for up to a week, but in a captive situation most incubating males are seen off the nest each night. The interval a male spends away from the nest appears to decrease as hatching time approaches; the male also loses a significant percentage of his bodyweight during the incubation period.

In the tight confines of the burrow, the fragile, thin-shelled egg is vulnerable to damage, and it is a reasonably common occurrence in captivity for eggs to be punctured by the parents' toenails or fractured through clumsy behaviour. Often very little remains of eggs damaged in this way, as the contents are eaten by the parents. Because of this risk of damage, and also the unreliability of some incubating males, it is the practice of many keepers to uplift eggs at some stage after the third week of incubation and transfer them to be artificially incubated. Taking eggs in this manner often stimulates the female to re-cycle and lay again thereby multiplying the breeding potential of captive pairs.

The egg hatches somewhere between 60 and 90 days, with 75 days being the average; during this period the egg's weight will have decreased by more than 11 per cent as water, produced by metabolism, evaporates from the egg.

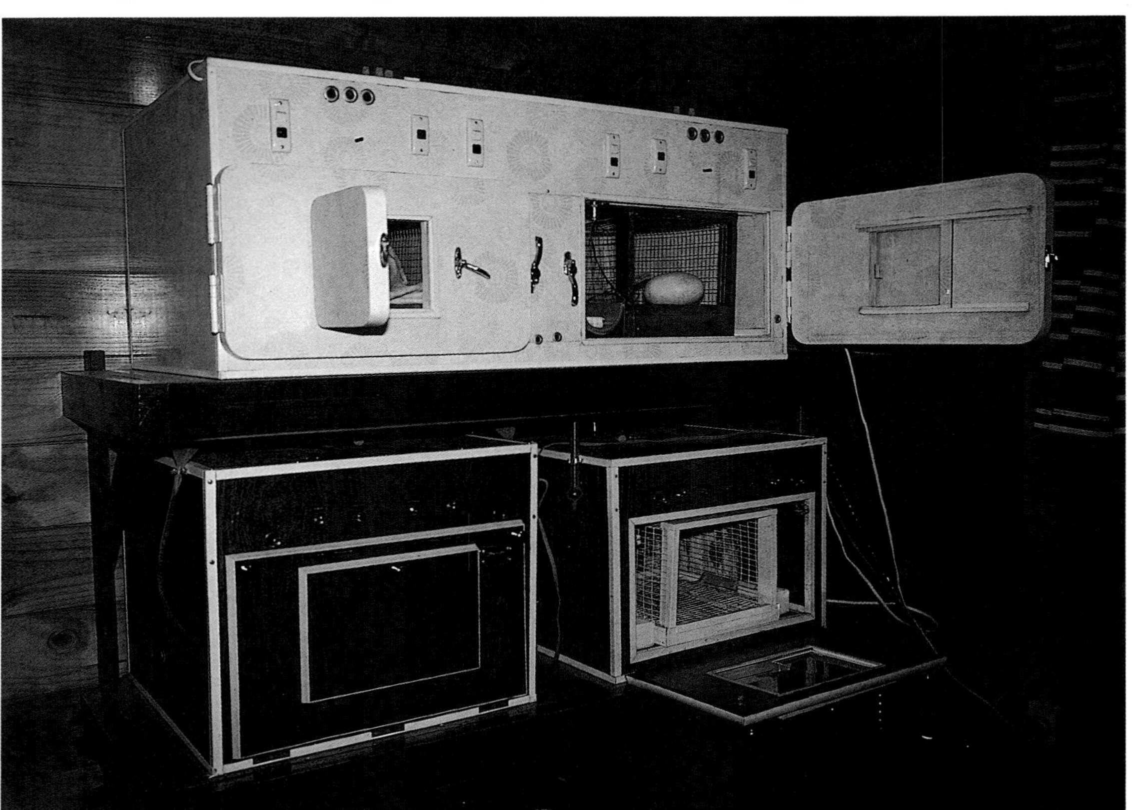

Kiwi egg incubators designed by Barry Rowe; note double doors for inspection or access, cradle around egg and front mounting of all controls.

In the latter third of incubation, the embryo is quite active, and if the egg is placed on a smooth, flat surface, it will often rock about. The kiwi chick has no egg tooth and cannot chip its way out of the shell in the typical avian manner. After piercing the air-cell membrane about 48 hours before actually hatching, the chick rests up and then begins thrusting, braced by its powerful feet, breaking the shell apart to gain its freedom. At this stage of its life, after such a long incubation period, the newly hatched kiwi chick is in a very advanced state of development.

Just prior to hatching, an artificially incubated kiwi egg requires high humidity (more than 85 per cent) to enable the chick to pierce the otherwise tough inner-shell membranes. It is assumed that incubating males duplicate this by re-entering the nest with wet plumage. In the incubator, wet towels are commonly used to boost the humidity and then provide the newly hatched chick with a soft padding. The freshly hatched kiwi chick has been described as 'an egg without a shell', owing to the large proportion of yolk sack still to be absorbed. The belly is so distended with yoke that the chick cannot move for the first two to three days, the yolk being used up at the rate of about one gram per hour.

Kiwi brooder designed by Barry Rowe, featuring inspection panel, separate compartments and slide-out bases.

The chick also hatches coated in a layer of jelly-like slime, which probably serves the function of protecting it from being chilled by cooling too rapidly. This slime dries and flakes off within 24 hours, revealing the kiwi chick to be already fully feathered. From three to four days after hatching, the chick will have absorbed enough of the yolk sack to enable it to shuffle about. At this stage the incubator-hatched chick can be transferred to a brooder to continue development.

At Otorohanga, the former director, Barry Rowe, developed both incubators and brooders suitable for kiwi use, and these designs have now become the standard type used in most rearing facilities. The brooder has two separate compartments linked by a doorway, the smaller compartment is darkened and heated from above, the chick spending its next few days on a padded base in this area. Heat control, an inspection window and a light all feature in this design to allow the keeper to monitor the chick at this delicate stage with a minimum of interference.

The other compartment of the brooder is covered with several centimetres of fresh top soil, leaves and grass sods and is unheated. By the seventh night the chick will have ventured away from the heat and into this area, fossicking about for small pieces of stone and twigs, preparing the gizzard for food, which it begins to procure the following evening. Just prior to its first feed, the eight-day-old chick will have lost an average 25 per cent of its bodyweight; this it regains within the next fifteen days. Barry Rowe recorded a kiwi chick as consuming between 200 and 300 earthworms during its first night of feeding!

Over the next five weeks the brooder heat source can be phased out gradually, and the chick grows rapidly, reaching a weight of one kilogram within six months. It is normal procedure to transfer the young birds to a grassed rearing pen after heating has been discontinued, as by this stage the chick will have outgrown its brooder. A smaller replica of the artificial burrow is provided and by this time the chick should have accepted, and been weaned onto, an artificial diet, although obviously the grassed pen will provide for a degree of natural foraging.

It is interesting to note that during the first six weeks or so, chicks will often be seen foraging during daylight hours oblivious to the light; however, after this age, they, like the adult kiwis, avoid light and become almost exclusively nocturnal.

DIET

Through the observations made on both wild and captive foraging birds and also analysis of gut contents, researchers have assessed the kiwi to be an omnivorous, opportunistic feeder. A large daily intake of food is required: in the case of the brown kiwi, estimated at some 400 grams bulk weight, made up of invertebrate life and plant material. Food is procured on or below the forest floor, and location and seasonal variations must dictate food type and abundance to some degree.

In a captive situation, even with the largest of possible enclosures, it would be practically impossible to provide enough natural food for a pair of kiwis, therefore additional substitute food must be provided. Many artificial diets have been formulated, and almost every establishment holding kiwis has its own recipe. Most have a meat base to provide sufficient protein, to which is added a cereal, usually in the form of a porridge, providing a viscous, soupy mix that enables the birds to ingest the food easily and also prevents the meat from drying out. Regardless of what ingredients are used, virtually all recipes include the addition of a pre-mix vitamin and mineral supplement, formulated in New Zealand by I.C.I. Tasman Laboratories especially for use by kiwis.

An interesting point to note is that the kiwi, having such a long probing bill, has difficulty in picking up certain food shapes. This problem requires slicing up of the food items into long, thin 'julienne' strips, most closely resembling the earthworms, larvae and grubs that make up a large part of the natural diet.

A certain degree of natural foraging occurs, and this at least partially compensates for any component lacking in the artificially formulated diets. Over the years, as newly formulated products come on the market and shortcomings of others become evident, diets are modified, the most recent possible problem being traces of pesticides being found in some foods. Use of fresh fruits and grains is becoming more evident in diets, and the recent accessibility of a number of insect types produced commercially has also meant a greater variety of food types available in New Zealand. At Otorohanga, several attempts have been made to broaden the diet even further by heavily planting enclosures with native plant species and increasing the amount of decomposing material in them. Experiments are also being carried out using soya-bean-based protein alternatives, which in the form of 'tofu' bean curd has met with very good acceptance by the kiwis used in the trial.

DISEASES AND PARASITES

Kiwis are extremely hardy birds and succumb to very few ailments, particularly if being maintained in an outdoor location. Birds in nocturnal houses are susceptible to respiratory infections if correct ventilation and humidity are not maintained. Care must be taken to ensure fine or dusty substrate materials are not used, as these could be inhaled into the lungs or cause blockages in the long olfactory tubes. To avoid this problem, regular misting of the enclosure to keep it damp is important. Sand, sawdust or seedy hay are unsuitable substrate or nestbox materials, the same applying to their use in carrying boxes. Kiwis are also stressed by subjection to light, and it is important to keep carrying boxes dark and well ventilated. The ventilation slats should be designed so as not to cause damage to the kiwi's bill; materials such as wire netting are unsuitable in carrying boxes and for enclosure walls.

Most wild kiwis carry a number of external and internal parasites. Normally, the parasite burden does not greatly affect the bird, unless other influences, such as injury or stress through capture, cause additional pressures. It is usual practice to reduce the parasite burden on newly acquired kiwis to a level where they do not overtake the birds' capacity to resist. Several species of tick, lice and mite live under the kiwi's thick, shaggy coat and can be eliminated using proprietary insecticide sprays or dusts.

Intestinal worms of three types have been recorded as parasitising kiwis: these being nematodes, cestodes and a species of trematode. Oral drenching for this form of parasite will usually reduce the burden.

The life span of kiwis in captivity is quite long compared with many other bird species. The majority of captive-held kiwis live more than ten years, and some are known to have lived on to more than 20 years. A female kiwi known to be 18 years of age was recorded as still laying.

RESEARCH

Because it displays so many divergent characteristics, the kiwi has long been of great interest to researchers; the nocturnal, burrowing habits, though, have precluded much research being carried out under natural conditions. Recently, the more widespread use of electronic devices has assisted greatly in the task of study in the wild. Captive kiwis have played a much greater role for study purposes, and the majority of aviary birds have been under scientific gaze for some part of their lives.

Researchers from all over the world have involved some aspect of the kiwi in their avian studies, and quite a formidable amount is now known about the species. The contribution to knowledge made from captive birds has been great in the area of reproduction, and most of this study has taken place within the last fifteen years. Such data as eggshell-pore geometry, lipid and amino acid composition of the egg contents, oxygen uptake and energy consumption during embryo development, energy value of the yolk reserve in a kiwi chick, and weight changes in a female's laying cycle have all been quantified.

Otorohanga Kiwi House is fortunate in having suitable study facilities, funded largely by the New Zealand Lotteries Board. These have been used extensively by visiting overseas scientists, students and Wildlife Service personnel for the last ten years, as well as by Otorohanga's own staff. Consequently, this centre has been at the forefront of much research into kiwis.

Initial research at Otorohanga centred on the egg, there being a need for even the most basic information so that a breeding and management plan could be adopted for captive birds. Over a period of years, kiwi breeding at Otorohanga and elsewhere had resulted in very few birds being hatched and raised by their parents.

The then-director at Otorohanga, Barry Rowe, set about determining the kiwi egg incubation data by the use of an electronic dummy egg. The egg was placed under a particularly obliging male to give Rowe a series of readings on egg temperature. Sensors placed at different points within the dummy egg revealed several interesting facts. First, it was discovered that kiwi eggs incubate at a lower temperature than most other birds (35°C as opposed to 39° for poultry), this is no doubt due to the body temperature of the kiwi, which is about 2° lower than that of other birds, and more closely resembles that of mammals. It was next learned that the kiwi egg was subject to a temperature gradient between top and bottom of some 10°, and there was an overall further temperature drop during the night. Other data obtained through the use of the electronic egg was a clear indication that the kiwi was

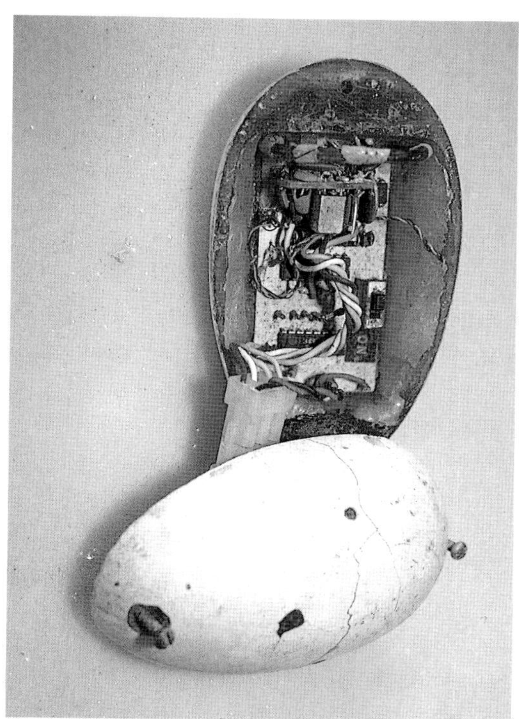

Electronic egg used at Otorohanga to determine correct incubation temperature for artificially incubating kiwi eggs.

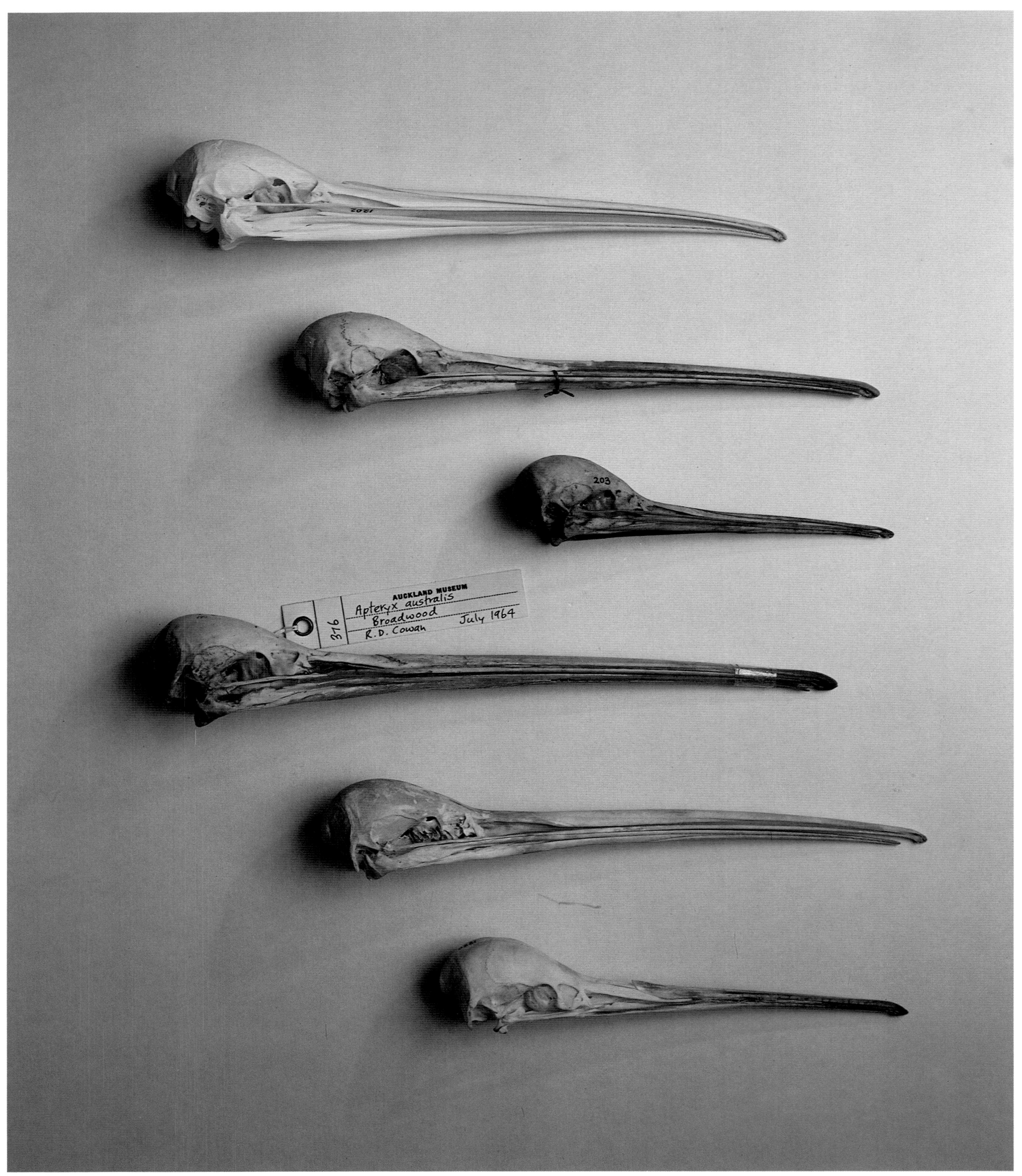

Skulls of brown kiwi, *Apteryx australis*, and little spotted kiwi, *Apteryx owenii*, lateral view.
Auckland Institute and War Memorial Museum
Photo: Jaan Voot

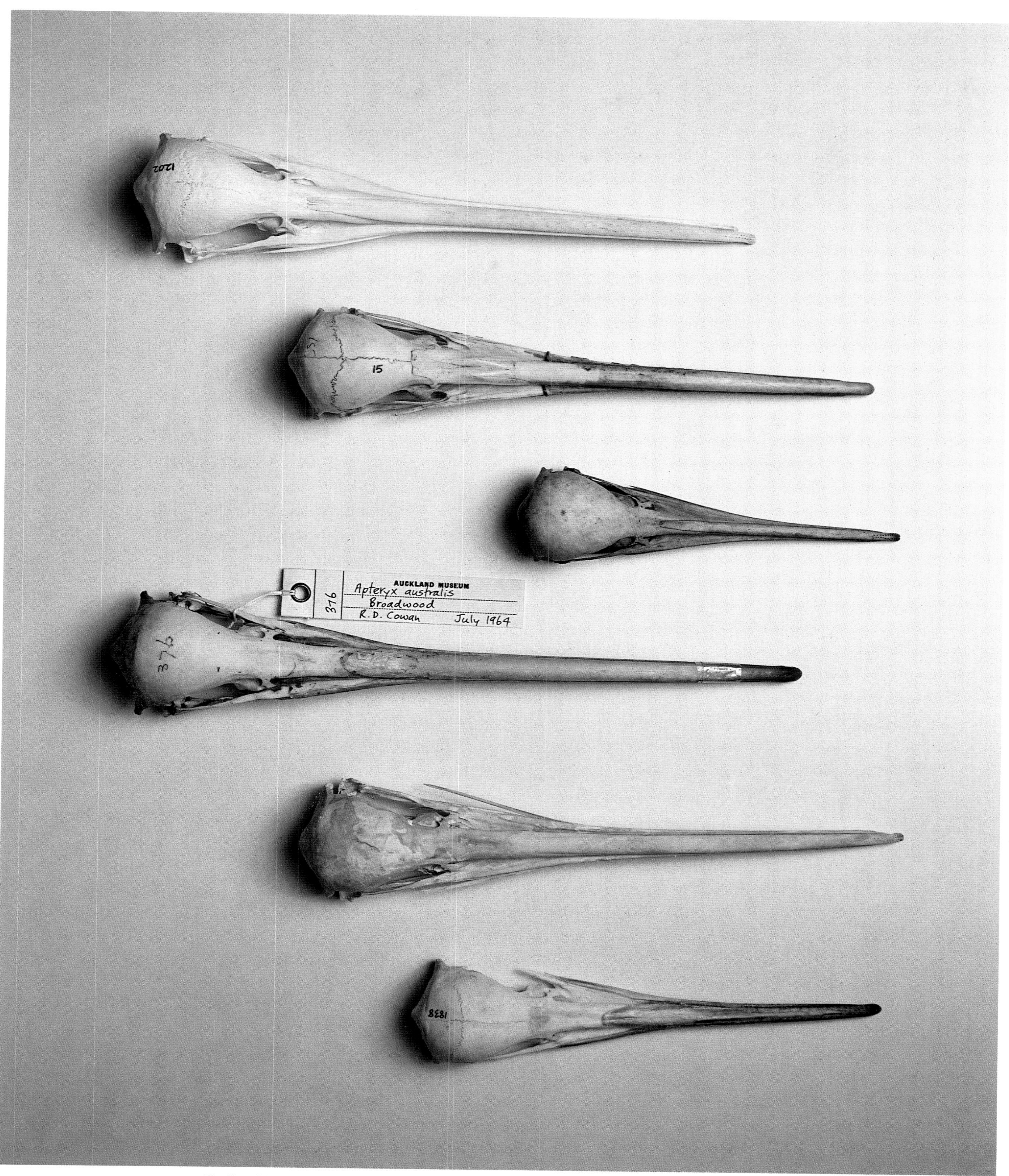

Skulls of brown kiwi, *Apteryx australis*, and little spotted kiwi, *Apteryx owenii*, dorsal view.
Auckland Institute and War Memorial Museum
Photo: Jaan Voot

not turning its egg, apart from an incidental shuffle, and that the air cell at the large end of the egg sits uppermost throughout the incubation period.

Rowe was able to test his results by setting up a still-air incubator to mimic the temperature gradient recorded under the male. The first egg test run in this incubator resulted in a successful hatching after 71 days' incubation. A visiting American professor, Dr William A. Calder III, assisted Rowe in these experiments and also carried out his own research into kiwi reproductive biology. After the artificial hatching of the first kiwi chick, many of the previous difficulties in the captive breeding of this species were overcome and kiwis have since bred at Otorohanga, and more recently at Auckland and Wellington Zoos on a regular basis. Several years of breeding kiwis by both artificial and, to a lesser degree, natural means at Otorohanga resulted in the compilation in 1978 of the first captive management manual on kiwis, authored by Barry Rowe and Brian Reid, the New Zealand Wildlife Service's kiwi research scientist.

This report has been used widely in both New Zealand and overseas and is a credit to the twelve years of pioneering research and dedication that Barry Rowe put into kiwi study.

CONSERVATION — THE ROLE OF AVICULTURE

The last few years have seen many zoos and bird parks change their orientation from 'exhibiting' species in rows of concrete-floored pens to one where the emphasis is on 'displaying' species in an appropriate habitat setting. There is also a greater emphasis placed on holding viable breeding groups of a particular species, as opposed to simply having that type represented somewhere in the collection. Often there are 'off-limit' breeding groups to back up the display group, thus providing a wider gene pool to draw on.

Sometimes, zoos go to great lengths and expense to obtain mates for individuals of rare species living on their own. Zoo management is becoming more aware of responsibility to preserve species, and within the constraints of its financial situation, a zoo will continually update its enclosures and other facilities to provide conducive breeding conditions. Progress in the area of dietary knowledge and veterinary care also means the breeding and longevity potential of captive-held birds is now much greater than it has been.

As species become more scarce in their diminishing natural habitats, greater pressure and importance will be put on the institutions holding birds to place conservation priorities first. The role of educating the public on the plight of the world's threatened animal species will also fall more heavily on zoological establishments. Assuming that the majority of zoos are responding to these conservation issues, any zoo fortunate enough to be holding kiwis has a role to play now, as these birds are threatened species in many parts of their range.

The high demand for kiwis by overseas zoos will no doubt continue in the future, although there are unlikely to be many birds exported to meet the demand. Presently, 90 per cent of all captively held kiwis belong to the North Island brown subspecies. The two spotted kiwi species are not kept outside New Zealand and account for less than twelve of the hundred or so kiwis in avicultural collections. Pairs of the South Island and Stewart Island brown kiwi species are not currently held in any collections.

It is a rare occurrence for kiwis to breed in a display (reversed day/night) situation, therefore zoos holding birds in this way are contributing very little to preserving the species and at best can only hope to fulfil an educational role.

Parks with breeding facilities producing kiwis on a regular basis have so far only been supplying other establishments with their progeny; to date no captive-bred birds have been liberated in the wild. This programme is at least allowing the captive population of North Island brown kiwis to remain genetically viable, with a small exchange of this subspecies being carried out between New Zealand and overseas zoos. The great spotted kiwi has only recently been bred in captivity for the first time at the National Wildlife Centre, Mount Bruce and at Otorohanga it is now possible that this species could gain a foothold in captivity, but there is still much progress to be made from an avicultural perspective. Great spotted kiwis are fascinating birds and display a bold, fearless approach. They excavate large burrows in comparison with the other two species and, at Otorohanga, are the kiwis most likely to be seen earliest in the evening.

The little spotted kiwi has an even more tenuous avicultural record, being a shy, generally nervous bird that takes a long adjustment period to captive conditions. Otorohanga has recently hatched its first chick after a lengthy 94-day incubation period by the male. The only other records of this species breeding naturally were at Mount Bruce in the mid-1970s. The other two brown kiwi subspecies would probably react similarly to the North Island brown in captivity, should the opportunity to keep them become available.

From an educational viewpoint, there are enough kiwis on display world-wide to allow millions of people the opportunity to see and learn something of these unique birds. Each zoo uses its own techniques to disseminate knowledge, ranging from simple to elaborate wall graphics, taped commentary or personally guided tours, written pamphlets and school project sheets. With so many interesting facets to the kiwi, the subject of its preservation often rates fairly low, but it is an area to which more attention should be paid by zoo staff.

In New Zealand, the preservation issue is of great importance, as the destruction of kiwi habitat goes on daily. In general, New Zealanders know very little about their national bird, and the educational role of kiwi displays cannot be overestimated. Major companies are responsible for much of the current habitat destruction in New Zealand, and it will take great public pressure to bring about the changes needed to preserve wild places. Therefore, it is of utmost importance that the public is made aware and kept informed of the kiwi's plight in the hope that pressure will stop the continuing destruction.

Recently, through public donations, the Otorohanga Zoological Society, along with the assistance of several other conservation organisations, was instrumental in purchasing a block of bushland in Northland now known as the Tangiteroria Kiwi Reserve. This reserve has become New Zealand's first bush area specifically saved and set aside for the preservation of kiwis. If it had not been purchased, the land would have speedily been cleared for grazing or exotic (pine) forestry. Such clearing would have resulted in the destruction of the more than 50 kiwis known to inhabit the reserve.

Kiwis are very vulnerable to clearing operations and many simply die in their burrows crushed by the bulldozer, or are carved up in the ensuing root-raking operations. Those that do manage to survive are often incinerated in the burn-offs that follow clearing, or are left to starve in a barren wasteland where the earth has dried out and the food supply diminished.

In view of this scenario, members of the Otorohanga Zoological Society and the Royal Forest and Bird Protection Society have gone into areas ahead of, or during, clearing operations and rescued kiwis, transferring them to protected bushlands and reserves. The exercise is not as straightforward as it may seem, as liaison with forestry companies on where the next areas are to be cleared is often hard to achieve. Even when it is known that a block is to be cleared, it is time-consuming work locating and retrieving kiwis from their underground haunts. To speed up the operation, trained labrador dogs are used to seek out kiwis by following their scents, the muzzled dogs inflicting no harm on the birds.

Over one hundred kiwis have since been found and relocated using this technique, and monitoring of these has shown that many have become established successfully in their new territories. Kiwis liberated on Arthur Cowan's property near Otorohanga, an area that has not held kiwis for more than 50 years, were recently observed breeding and are regularly heard in the vicinity of the farmhouse. Other protected reserves containing relocated kiwis in the central North Island area appear to have been successful, as campers in these areas often report hearing kiwis at night.

Although such salvage work and purchasing of bush blocks may not be regarded as normal activities for most zoos, it is certainly an area where zoological expertise can be put to good practical use. In the foreseeable future it may also prove one of the best methods to assist in the preservation of viable groups of kiwis as their habitat comes under increasing pressure. The releasing of zoo-bred stock is not presently a feasible alternative, because, as previously mentioned, sufficient numbers are not being bred.

Dr William Calder described the kiwi as an honorary mammal, and any person who has been fortunate enough to be associated with keeping kiwis can testify to their mammalian traits; for instance, the heavy reliance kiwis place on a sense of smell as they hover about your feet sniffing and snorting at feeding time, or the cat-like snarling when they are agitated, and the soft grunting noises as they pad about or become engrossed in excavating a new burrow. Some males are so strongly territorial they attempt to chase the intruding person off their property by kicking and tugging on trouser legs, undaunted by the far greater size of the invader.

There is no valid reason why the brown and great spotted kiwis need become endangered species as has already happened to the little spotted kiwi and many other endemic New Zealand birds. It is vitally important that a species regarded by New Zealanders as their national bird, adopted by the rest of the world as representing and typifying New Zealanders, and awarded a special status by scientists and ornithologists should not suffer this fate. It is to be hoped that aviculture can play an increasing role in preserving this species for the benefit of future generations.

10

THE KIWI AND ITS EGG

The earth is inhabited by about 9,000 species of birds. Of these, the kiwis are among the most unusual, from egg through adulthood. Characteristics such as a well-developed sense of smell via nostrils at the tip of the oral probe, shaggy plumage that looks and functions like fur and burrowing habits make them seem quite mammalian — on an island subcontinent that lacks native terrestrial mammals.

Kiwis are the smallest of the ratite birds, all of which are flightless. The name 'ratite' refers to their raft-like breastbones, the keel of the sternum (characteristic of fliers) assumed to have been lost. Sometime in the past, perhaps before Gondwanaland broke up, the ancestor(s) of the other ratites (ostriches, emus, cassowaries and rheas) exceeded the theoretical maximum size for self-propelled flight. As weight increases, flight power requirements increase out of proportion to the power available from the pectoral muscles; doubling the weight of a bird requires more than twice as much power to get airborne. Kiwis, however, are not too big to fly, but though smaller than many proficient flyers they have not regained flight (if indeed their ancestors did actually fly).

Discussion concerning the relationships and evolution of the ratites has not been without controversy. In attempting to reconstruct the phylogeny of the ratites, several lines of evidence have been utilised, including the egg. For example, Osuga and Feeney examined physical and chemical properties of egg white proteins of the ratites. Prager and her co-workers used the albumen protein ovotransferin and immunological distances to reconstruct the phylogeny of the ratites. They found an 'almost simultaneous divergence into three lineages . . . tinamou, ostrich, and other ratites . . .' from a monophyletic past. This had certain general similarities with Cracraft's reconstruction based on morphology, except that the rheas and ostriches were more widely separated immunologically whereas rheas were closer to kiwis, morphologically. The breathing pores in kiwi eggshell are of a simple double-ended funnel shape, unlike those of all the other ratites, in which there is branching as the pores proceed outward. In this regard, the kiwi eggshell is similar to that of the tinamous (Tinamidae) flying birds of Central and South America, which are thought, in some evolutionary reconstructions, to be closely related to the ancestral stock of the ratites. The brown kiwi and the emu have the same number of chromosomes and share ancient karyotypes. Skeletal features indicate affinities between moas and kiwis.

If all birds descended from a pigeon-sized *Archaeopteryx*-like ancestor, the evolution of ratites has involved a scale-up of body dimensions. If the ratites are a monophyletic group, and if the kiwis descended from the moas, they must have gone through a secondary scale-down. When the evolution of a lineage involves a scale-up or scale-down in overall body size, the many necessary alterations are not all in the same proportions. However, the kiwi egg seems to have been overlooked in the re-scaling from moa to present adult size.

Flightlessness, probing the forest floor for earthworms, nesting in underground burrows, incubation by males — each of these *qualitative* peculiarities can be seen in one or another kind of bird, the takahe (*Notornis*), woodcock (*Scolopax*), shearwaters (Procellariidae), and phalaropes (*Phalaropus* spp.), respectively. The diversity of birds can also be considered in a series of *quantitative* patterns in fundamental dimensions of mass, length, time and temperature.

Egg size, incubation period and condition of the hatchling are basic to the description of each bird's life history. Measurements of yolk mass, shell thickness and rate of water loss through the shell pores are prerequisites for understanding egg function. Data for these variables from hundreds of species of birds reduce to neat and consistent patterns. We seem to have both a basis for generalisations and a strong suggestion that evolution must work within some physical constraints.

A marked exception from these supposed constraints — the odd species that fails to conform to the patterns — could make us suspect either its measurements or the generalisations. If the measurements are confirmed, this provides a great case history for evolutionary speculation. Our understanding is challenged; 'comparative studies' are warranted. What does qualify the kiwis as most unusual is their quantitative peculiarities; kiwis are 'off the lines'. These differences are revealed by comparing the brown kiwi (*Apteryx australis*) with predictions from biological scaling for a 'typical' bird of the same size. This will seem reminiscent of the old question, 'what came first, the chicken or the egg?' — or 'what came first, this feature of the egg or that?'. In nature, of course, they had to come together, to function at every stage in the evolution.

BIOLOGICAL SCALING

Quantitative comparisons are made most expediently using body size as the quantitative reference. Of all the features of birds that one might describe, the most profoundly influential is body size. Among other factors, size determines what an animal needs, what it can do and how long it will take to be done. We can describe the colours, beak and feet shapes, habitats, diets, etc., but when it comes to summarising or predicting food requirements, egg sizes, incubation periods or lifespans, no characteristic is as useful as body mass ('weight') as an expression of size. In terms of life's requirements and opportunities, matters of big versus little, fast versus slow, etc., are not so much a case of traditional, qualitative 'either/or' distinctions, but gradations in the continuum have encompassed an array of design problems and patterns increasingly recognised as important in many areas of basic and applied biology: physiology, functional morphology, ecology, growth and development, pharmacokinetics, gerontology, prosthetics, wildlife management and biological oceanography.

Had geometry somehow worked differently, with area increasing by the same factor as volume, we would have isometry (literally, of the same measurements), but in reality, we have allometry (allo- = different or strange; metry = measurements), which Gould defined as 'the study of size and its consequences'.

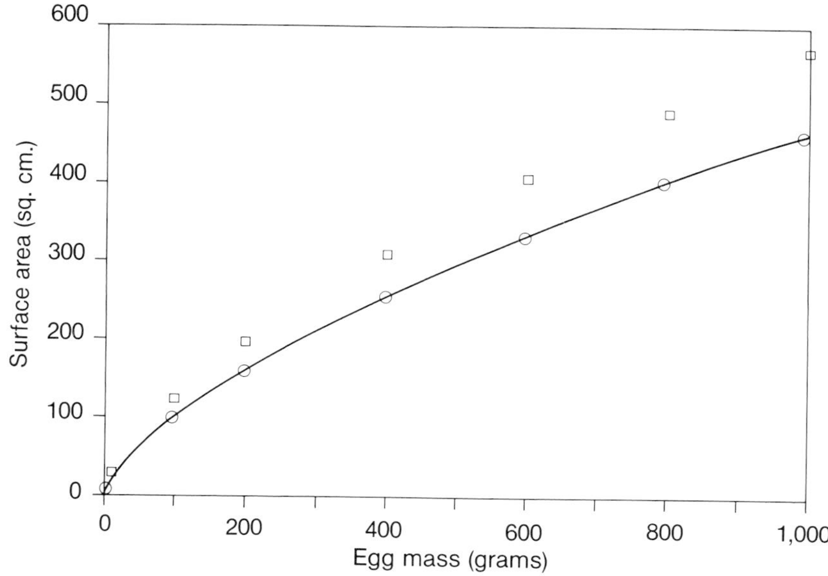

FIGURE 1 The surface areas of eggs (connected by curve) and cubes increase with mass of egg or cube, but by progressively smaller increments. This is a consequence of the geometry, surface area increasing not linearly but in proportion to the 2/3 power of volume or mass, regardless of shape of object.

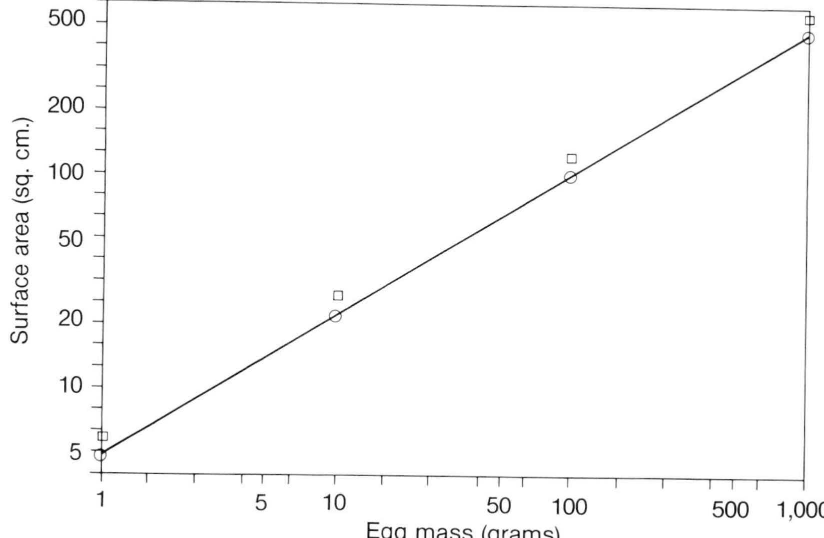

FIGURE 2 When the relationship between egg and cube masses and their surface areas is plotted on logarithmic scales, the curve of Figure 1 is transformed into a straight line, and the slope is equal to the exponent (2/3 power).

The scaling of surface area to the masses of cubes and eggs is seen in Figure 1. At the density of birds' eggs, a sphere presents the least surface area per unit mass. A cube will have 24 per cent more surface exposed. Elongation from sphere to egg will increase surface area by only 2 to 2.5 per cent, a difference too small to show up well when a large mass range is portrayed. Note that the use of logarithmic scales, as in Figure 2, converts an exponential curve to a straight line.

BIRD EGGS IN GENERAL

The ovum, consisting of germ cell and yolk, is formed in the hen's ovary. How much of the completed egg mass is yolk depends upon how far development is to proceed before hatching. Birds born blind, naked and helpless come from eggs with about 20 per cent yolk. The more advanced development of downy precocial young capable of self-feeding are produced from eggs of 35 per cent yolk.

After ovulation and yolk deposition, the albumen, membranes and shell are added as the egg passes down the oviduct. Apparently to reduce weight for flight, most birds retain only one ovary, usually the left. Both ovaries are present in the chick, as in all other female vertebrates, but one gradually atrophies in most species. Kiwis are among the 1 per cent of bird species that retain both ovaries functionally, the two taking turns producing eggs.

The disastrous effects of synthetic chlorinated hydrocarbons such as DDT and PCBs in eggshell 'thinning' that led to squashed eggs and cessation of reproduction, gave dramatic indication of the importance of the shell. Considering the value of poultry and eggs as a source of protein and iron for mankind, a full understanding of how the shell functions in respiration and water conservation would seem of vital importance. This was ignored until the 1970s, when Hermann Rahn and his co-workers began an elegant series of studies of bird eggs. They stimulated interest in egg physiology, culminating in international symposia volumes of great significance. Thus the egg physiologists have made a monumental contribution to ornithology, from outside its traditional boundaries.

In general, the larger the bird, the larger the egg, but the ratio of egg to body size is not the same for all birds. A 3.5-gram hummingbird lays an egg that is 14 per cent of its body weight, while the egg of an ostrich weighs only 1.5 per cent of the female's weight. Other characteristics of eggs also scale non-linearly. A larger egg has a greater daily water loss and a longer incubation period, but the product of water-loss rate per day and number of days of incubation, i.e., total evaporation from hatching to fledging, is a similar fraction of fresh egg weight, 13–18 per cent. This provides the air space from which the chick will draw its first breath.

The water leaves the egg as vapour, which diffuses out the same pores through which the oxygen diffuses in for the respiration of the developing embryo. The larger or more numerous the pores, the faster oxygen can enter, but the faster water can escape. Thus information on porosity can be obtained from water loss as determined by weighing. This porosity ultimately limits inward diffusion of oxygen, so it can in turn be used to predict the oxygen consumption or metabolic rate of the chick just before hatching.

Such a general picture is satisfying. With so many clearly established relationships, we not only understand the functional processes better, but it would appear that evolution has occurred within some rather general guidelines or constraints. That is to say, natural selection has engineered rather closely the size of the egg, the management of water within, and gas exchanges with the outside, even the structural characters.

If these relationships are such faithful and necessary correlates, how did the kiwi get by with its oversized egg (20 per cent of adult female weight) and extremely long incubation of 71 to 84 days? Do we understand the rules of evolutionary scaling, or are these really 'rules' if some birds are exempt? Was the slow incubation the result of poor contact between relatively small adult male (who does the incubating) and relatively large egg? Was nature confused in the process of scaling up from the ancestral flying bird to the moa-kiwi ancestor and then scaling back down to the size of the domestic fowl?

We will rely upon the published allometry for birds and bird eggs, also some intensity characteristics such as temperature and percentage composition which do not show any size-dependent trends. These equations include large-sample egg/body size relationships; (adult metabolic rate allometry; water loss from eggs; the interdependence of gaseous permeabilities of eggshells, incubation time and egg mass; mass of shell, yolk and albumen; egg-cooling constants; and total energy cost of growth, embryonic maintenance and hatching. Using these, one can predict from egg mass the incubation time, oxygen uptake rate, porous conduction to water vapour, shell thickness and weight and total water loss during incubation. The ease or difficulty by which water vapour moves through the porous shell (water vapour conductance) is measured, quite simply, as mass loss under controlled humidity. Knowing the vapour conductance, one can predict reliably the oxygen consumption of the chick just before it hatches.

The peculiarities of kiwis can be appreciated by comparing them quantitatively with predictions for a kiwi-sized (2.5-kilogram) bird from allometric equations for typical birds (excluding the Passeriformes, which have metabolic rates considerably higher than all other homeotherms). In the discussion to follow, comparison will be made to predictions for an 'allometrically typical' 2.5-kilogram bird or 436-gram egg (for a 'typical' egg of that size from a larger bird), from the appropriate equations of these and other authors, so that the degree of non-conformity in kiwi oviparity can be evaluated. Note that unless otherwise stated, the species referred to hereafter is the brown kiwi, the only one sufficiently common for extensive study.

THE OVER-SIZED KIWI EGG

Sir Julian Huxley pioneered the application of allometry to biology of growth. He showed that logarithmically transformed data points for other ratite birds fell neatly on a straight line. Even though the log-log plot visually minimises differences, the egg-weight for *Apteryx* is far above what would be its appropriate position based on body size (Figure 3). As unusual as the kiwi and its egg were, four decades passed before they were to attract further scientific study. The original relationship of log-egg-mass versus log-bird-mass described by Huxley has been progressively refined by enlarging the data base. Eggs from wild brown kiwis, larger than those studied in captivity, average 436 grams, nearly four times the prediction.

Natural selection seems to have been quite practical. Energy costs and physical constraints preclude random caprice. Some variations work. Others would not and had they cropped up, would have been eliminated as maladaptive. The principle of symmorphosis says that animals are reasonably designed with adequate, but not excessive, capacity. Does the kiwi's egg violate symmorphosis? To decide that it is not excessive in size would involve circular reasoning: it is just the right size because it was not selected against! The 2.5-kilogram brown kiwi's egg remained at a size appropriate for a 14.3-kilogram moa. Cracraft supposed that 'during phylogeny the kiwi lineage became smaller in body size but a larger egg remained advantageous.' Gould pointed out that the within-species scaling of egg size with body size of domestic hens (mass$^{0.15}$) might have applied as the kiwi descended from its moa ancestor. Hence the moa egg and moa might have been bigger than the 436 gram and 14.3 kilogram respectively.

The natural selection of egg size has doubtlessly been influenced by several factors, such as food supply during egg-formation and after hatching, danger of predation, development rate and degree before hatching, adult body size, clutch size and ancestry. The evolutionary ecologist can make simplifying assumptions, such as that we 'assume that the eggs should be laid at a size which yields the maximum growth rate on the parental investment' (Stearns). However, the ratio, hatching mass/fresh egg mass for two kiwi chicks was 48 and 56 per cent, excluding internalised yolk from hatchling mass, compared with 54 per cent predicted for the 'typical' 2.5-kilogram bird.

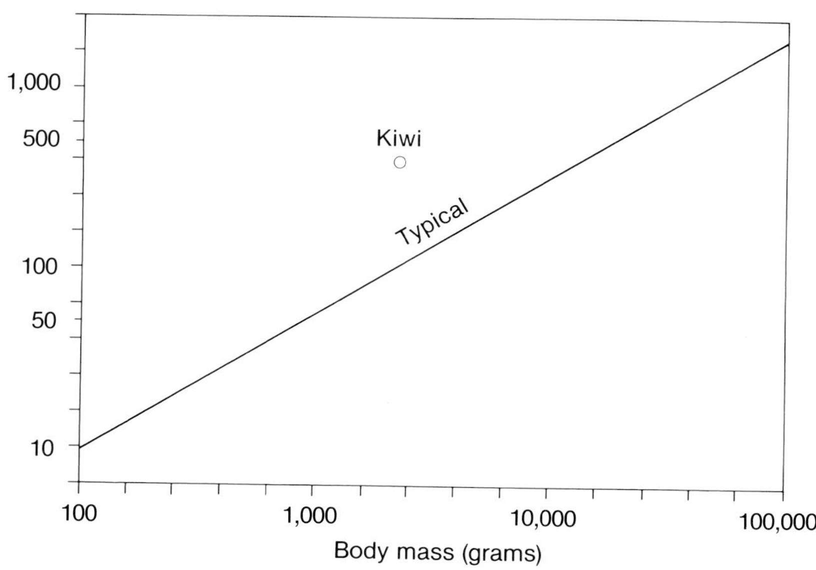

FIGURE 3 Egg mass as a function of the body mass of the bird species. Even on log-log co-ordinates, the kiwi is obviously far off the curve for typical birds.

The allometry for egg characteristics and functions has been derived on the basis of egg mass instead of adult mass; the predictions which follow will be for a 'typical' 436-gram egg.

EGG-MAKER AND EGG-CARETAKER

The female kiwi puts all of her energetic effort into making the large egg. By the time she lays it in the burrow, her weight has decreased by more than the weight of the egg, owing to her fasting and metabolising some of her own tissues during the last two days of an egg cycle. She stands over the egg for a while, eventually leaving the burrow so the male can come and begin the two and a half months' incubation. The male leaves the burrow to feed once or twice a night. Some ornithologists have suggested that the female may bring some food to him.

A typical interval between the laying of two successive eggs is 24 days. Before an egg from one ovary is laid, the next egg from the opposite ovary will reach at most a diameter of 40 millimetres (estimated 35 grams). By the end of the first third of the cycle, the increase in body mass of the hen is enough to account for the total mass of a yolk.

From weight changes of a female kiwi during egg-formation monitored by Rowe at Otorohanga, it appeared that the energy-rich yolk is deposited in the first seven and a half days of the typically twenty-four-day egg synthesis cycle. Bomb calorimetry of infertile egg components made it possible to relate this to standard metabolism. The standard metabolic rate serves as a baseline for comparing the energetic demands of an animal's life. Allowing for the cost of synthesis, during this week the hen might add the equivalent of 174 to 203 per cent to her basal energy requirement, in addition to the costs of activity such as foraging.

EGG CONTENTS

Albumen, being 87 per cent water, is cheap and easy to acquire in a damp forest environment, so need not be carried around in the oviduct long in advance of ovulation. However, after the beginning of the breeding season, wild brown kiwis recovered little or no mass between layings of successive eggs. It is estimated that 40 per cent of the material deposited in each egg comes from body reserves.

The amount of energy-rich yolk (230–250 grams) in a kiwi egg is even farther from what would be predicted for a 2.5-kilogram bird. Whereas a typical precocial bird's egg would contain 39 per cent yolk, the kiwi egg has 61 to 65 per cent yolk. Another way to view this is that the kiwi's egg-yolk is as large as that produced by a 35-kilogram emu. Nine-tenths of the energy in a kiwi egg is in the yolk, which is six times as energy-rich per gram as albumen.

IS THE KIWI EGG SO RIDICULOUS AS IT SEEMS?

The most obvious nonconformity of the kiwi egg is its large size. On the inside, the yolk is disproportionately large. If you waited for the egg to hatch, the incubation period would seem unusually long. To go beyond those facts would require focus on finer details. The lesson from the avian egg studies of Rahn and his associates is that no detail exists in isolation; rather it is part of a finely tuned process. The collection of measurements (Table 1) makes it possible to evaluate the traits in kiwi reproduction. Though well known, we must remind ourselves of the goal of reproduction in a stable population: to attain replacement individuals of the same size in time to offset mortality. Is the formation of such a large amount of yolk wasteful and inefficient? Does the prolonged incubation reflect further inefficiency in use of time, energy, and in loss of water?

TABLE 1

The brown kiwi, her egg, and allometric predictions of what they 'should be' (as 2.5-kilogram non-passerine birds)

A. Based on body mass of 2.5 kilograms (except chick metabolism):			
Variable	*Kiwi*	*2.5 kg*	*Kiwi/2.5 kg*
Standard metabolism (kilojoules/day)	354	613	0.58
Egg size (grams)	436	115	3.81
Hatchling (grams)	331	61.9	5.34
Grams of chick per gram of egg	0.76	0.54	1.40
Chick less yolk (grams)	209	52.9	3.95
Standard metabolism of chick (kJ/day)	119	183	0.65
Based on fresh egg mass of 436 grams:			
Variable	*Kiwi egg*	*436 g egg*	*Kiwi egg/predicted*
Incubation period (days)	74	45	1.64
Shell (grams)	23	47	0.49
Shell thickness (mm)	0.47	0.75	0.63
Contents (grams)	413	389	1.06
energy (kjoules)	5062	3321	1.52
Yolk (grams)	252	156	1.62
energy (kjoules)	4579		
Albumen (grams)	161	234	0.69
energy (kjoules)	483		
Total oxygen uptake (to hatching, litres)	43.5		
energy (kjoules)	857	740	1.16
Spare yolk (grams)	123	22.7	7.06
energy (kjoules)	2247	318.7	5.39
Water vapour conductance			
(adjusted to 436 g egg) [mg/(Torr.da)]	30	49.4	0.61
(measured, mean 366 g)	26	47	0.60
(from shell structure; Silyn-Roberts 1983)	23.7	47	0.51
Shell pore cross-sectional area (sq. micrometers)	396.3	600.4	0.66
Pore density (per cm²)	40.5	73.9	0.55
Shell surface area (cm²)	263.9	270.2	
Total functional pore area (mm²)	4.3	13.4	0.32
calculated from water vapour loss (mm²)	5.2	13.4	0.39
Total water loss during incubation (%)	14.2	14.5	0.98
(mg water)	61.7	63.1	0.98
Energy (kJ/gram chick)	4.1	14.0	0.29
(per cent of egg stores)	16.9	22.3	0.76
Days incubation (pore area/shell thickness)			
(from water loss)	8187	8040	1.02
(from shell geometry)	6670	8040	0.83

Eggs of North Island brown kiwi, *Apteryx australis mantelli*, actual size.
Auckland Institute and War Memorial Museum
Photo: Jaan Voot

Eggs of great spotted kiwi, *Apteryx haastii*, (above) and little spotted kiwi, *Apteryx owenii*, (below), actual size.
Auckland Institute and War Memorial Museum
Photo: Jaan Voot

The typical precocial neonate is 2.1 per cent of adult mass (52.9/2500 grams). In comparison, the large egg of the kiwi gets the hatchling a lot farther along its growth trajectory, to 8.4 per cent of adult size (209 grams without yolk/2500-gram adult). The kiwi egg yields 1.4 times as much chick per gram of fresh egg mass as the typical counterpart, and uses less than a third as much energy per gram of hatchling. The average growth rate is 2.82 grams per day of incubation for the kiwi (209 grams/74 days) versus 1.19 grams per day (52.9 grams/45 days) if it had been 'normal'. This all seems to be 'good value'.

The incubation period is 64 per cent longer than it 'could have been', and if the shell porosity were the same as that for a 'typical' 436-gram egg, this would result in 64 per cent more water loss. In addition to that effect on water loss, the shell is only 63 per cent as thick as would be the case for a typical 436-gram egg. Thickness means two things: strength of shell and diffusion distance for gas exchanges, including the loss of water vapour.

The reduction in porosity has been confirmed by actual microstructural measurements. It is not so easy to quantify the reduction in porosity anatomically as to measure water escape as mass loss! Silyn-Roberts developed a new technique for making casts of the pores, and provided the necessary quantification of the porosity. She found that the number of pores was reduced to 53 per cent of the allometric prediction, and that the cross-sectional areas of individual pores were reduced to 66 per cent of the allometrically expected, combined for a total reduction to 35 per cent. Using her data in the equation for conductance to water vapour, she calculated a water vapour conductance that was only 8.7 per cent less than was actually measured from brown kiwi eggs, a remarkable agreement of form and function. Part of the apparent difference between these independent calculations may be due to unknown differences in egg sizes. However, it must be noted that there was enough variation in both sets of measurement to make the difference between 35 and 39 per cent statistically indistinguishable.

Further evidence of compensation in water vapour conductance is seen in estimating the water loss over the incubation period for Reid's chick. From 413 grams of egg contents, a wet chick of 351.3 grams emerged, so the difference of 61.7 grams was lost as evaporation, 14.2 per cent of fresh egg mass or 14.9 per cent of fresh egg contents, in close accord with the allometric prediction.

So far, we have found nothing wrong with the kiwi's way of oviparity, except that it takes longer. It is interesting that the resting or standard metabolic rate — the rate of energy expenditure while 'idling' — is considerably lower than what would be expected of a 'typical' non-passerine bird of 2.5-kilogram body mass — 61 per cent as a matter of fact. This makes it appear as if kiwi life is just at a more relaxed pace, taking an additional 64 to 73 per cent more time. Between embryonic turnover (incubation period) and adult turnover, there is juvenile metabolic turnover. The metabolism of a kiwi chick averaged 65 per cent of the prediction based on non-passerine size, perhaps elevated somewhat, at that, for the cost of growth.

Hence, despite the initial appearance of waste and inefficiency, the kiwi egg fits the principle of symmorphosis, that 'no more structure is formed and maintained than is required to satisfy functional needs' (Taylor and Weibel).

INCUBATION TIME AND TEMPERATURE

According to the equation of Hermann Rahn and Amos Ar, a 436-gram egg should require 45 days of incubation; it actually takes 74 to 84 days. Artificial incubation took only 71 days, without the nocturnal cooling that occurs when the incubating male goes out to feed. A captive male left his burrow for about 90 minutes once after dark and once in the early morning. During this time the temperature of a surrogate egg (with a cooling constant that matched that of a real egg) cooled sufficiently for a probable cessation of development for at least 1.75 hours per day. Over a 74-day incubation, this would add up to more than enough time to account for the difference between artificial and natural incubation times.

The gestation periods (pregnancy duration) of placental mammals average twice as long as the incubation periods of birds of the same body size, 80 to 98 days for kiwi size. It is often assumed that eggs, which may be unattended while the parent is feeding, have rapid incubations to reduce vulnerability, as contrasted with viviparity wherein the embryo is less vulnerable. Then the kiwi could survive with such a long incubation (indeed, one better predicted from mammalian gestation equations than by the equation for incubation periods of birds) because New Zealand had no mammalian predators that would enter a kiwi burrow.

Biochemical reaction rates underlying all of metabolism, growth and development are affected exponentially by temperature, such that a 10°C rise will increase the rate by a factor of two or more. (This ratio for a 10° change is called the Q_{10} effect.) Conversely, a lower temperature means slower biochemical progress. This raised the question of whether the 64 per cent longer incubation was due to lower temperatures, either from poor contact with an awkwardly large egg or the lower body temperatures of kiwis.

That question stimulated my first visit to the land of kiwis. Little did I know that Barry Rowe of the Otorohanga Zoological Society was already using a telemetry transmitter to record the temperature during incubation of a wax-filled eggshell. The egg temperatures, which averaged 35.4°C at embryo-depth were compared with temperatures maintained by a bantam domestic hen, incubating the same water-filled kiwi egg with telemetry device at 37.7°. These reflected the differences between body temperatures of 'typical' adult birds and the temperatures of adult brown kiwis. The basal temperatures of kiwis are 38°C, about 2° lower than typical birds and more like those of mammals. The lower body temperatures suggest lower metabolic levels in kiwis. If a small bantam could maintain a kiwi egg at 37.7°, the long incubation was not simply the result of the egg being too large for the brood-patch to keep warm!

The egg exhibited a marked temperature gradient to 26.6° at the bottom, perhaps sufficient for convection of fluid contents. We then used an epoxy-reinforced shell filled with water and a telemetry transmitter and recorded incubation temperatures of $35.4 \pm 0.7°$, verifying data from the wax-filled egg. When the water-filled egg was placed under a bantam domestic hen, it was maintained at 37.6–37.8°, although the air temperature was 3.5–4.5° cooler above ground than in the kiwi burrow. The lower incubation temperature of kiwis does not seem to be a consequence of the mismatch of big egg to small bird, because the bantam hen was even smaller than the kiwi.

The small difference between egg temperature during incubation (35°), brood patch temperature (37°) and body temperatures (38° indicates a good body-egg contact. In other species, the incubation temperature of eggs correlates well with the body temperature of the birds. Penguins and Procellariformes (shearwaters and petrels) have body temperatures that are lower than most birds, as are their incubation temperatures.

Perhaps the lower metabolic rate and, consequently, slower incubation could be attributed to the lower incubation temperature? If we assume a Q_{10} of

2.0 to 2.5, a reduction from domestic fowl to kiwi incubation temperatures could account for 39 to 51 per cent of the decrease in highest oxygen consumption before pipping, so the lower metabolic and development rates are not merely consequences of the lower incubation temperature compared to other birds.

Having determined the natural incubation temperature of kiwis, Rowe was able to achieve the first entirely artificial incubation of a kiwi egg, while I monitored oxygen consumption at two- to three-day intervals over the 71 days of artificial incubation (Figure 4). On the final week before the chick began to crack the shell, the oxygen consumption reached a value 63 per cent of that predicted allometrically for its original mass of 403 grams.

Did that reduction indicate a partial oxygen-deprivation? The answer came from measurements of oxygen consumption of the chick two weeks after hatching (when it had finally consumed the nearly half of its yolk that remained at hatching) and from two older chicks. The mean values for basal oxygen consumption were 65 per cent of what would be predicted for ordinary birds of their size. Five adult brown kiwis also showed significant reduction, compared with their predicted metabolic rates, and individuals of the other two species had quantitatively similar rates.

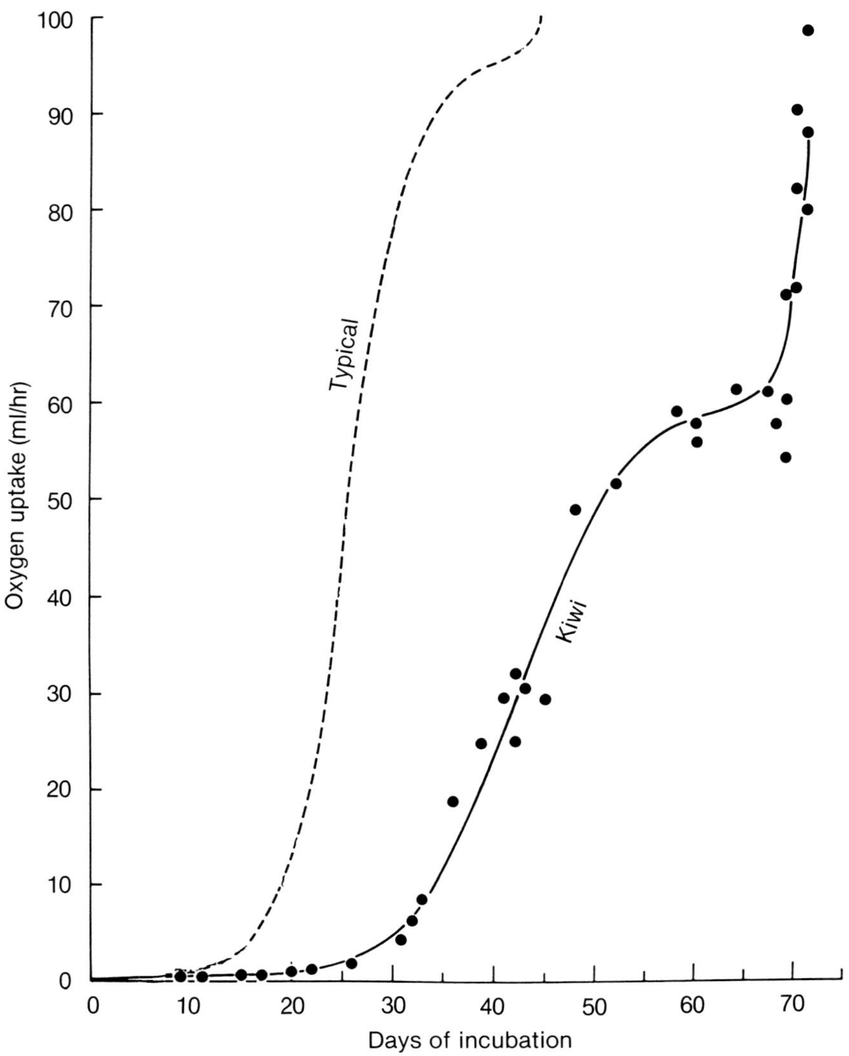

FIGURE 4 Oxygen consumption recordings of a 403 g egg of the brown kiwi as a function of incubation time. Curves fitted by visual inspection, solid to the data points, and dashed lines for values calculated allometrically for a 'typical' 403 g egg with 44 days of incubation. Note that the product of rate times time is total (cumulative) oxygen consumpton appearing as the area under a curve. The cumulative oxygen consumption is the same, whether high times fast or low times slow.

PROTECTING THE INVESTMENT

Given this enormous amount of stored energy in one egg and its long period of potential risk, it would be worthy, and in need, of special protection. There were no terrestrial mammalian predators until man and his companions arrived on the scene, but the brown kiwi is a resilient and aggressive defender of his eggs, reducing the extent of foraging time in the interest of nest-attentiveness and covering the burrow entrance with vegetation when leaving to feed.

The other threat to this rich egg is the penetration by heterotrophic bacteria. Kiwi eggs must represent a grand opportunity for invading microbes: a tremendous yolk for a culture, one of the longest incubation periods known, a disproportionately thin shell that is often and easily hair-line cracked, and exposure to bacteria and fungi in the damp underground burrow. What possible defences are provided in the egg-white proteins? The egg white of the brown kiwi contains unusually high concentrations of ovoinhibitor and lysozyme g. Ovotransferin constitutes 10 per cent of the egg-white proteins of kiwi, emu and cassowary, slightly more in eggs of tinamou, turkey and chicken, and considerably less in ostrich and rhea eggs, percentages not correlated with incubation period or egg size.

The kiwi egg white has several proteins in unusually high amounts. One, ovoinhibitor, is a broad-spectrum fungal proteinase with implied antimicrobial defence function, but direct evidence for this is lacking. Lysozyme g attacks peptidoglycans from gram-negative bacteria. Such bacteria have been found in rotten eggs of waterfowl. However, conclusive evidence for an important enzymatic role for lysozyme g in defending the egg is lacking. Ovomucin and lysozyme g form a gel structure, which may form a 'scaffolding' to centre the yolk in the albumen. This maximizes the distance through the viscous albumen as a barrier to microbial colonisation of the yolk. Ovotransferin ties up and transports iron, so it can deny bacterial access to free iron, so may be a principal antimicrobial defence.

While the above correlations between albumen protein concentrations and the large egg, large yolk and long incubation do not prove a causal linkage, they do suggest possible defence functions.

WHY IS THE EGGSHELL SO THIN?

An eggshell should be strong enough to resist forces from without, but not so strong that the chick cannot break through from within. The reabsorption of calcium carbonate from the shell by the embryonic circulation is probably relatively insignificant in the escape. In the domestic fowl's egg, reabsorption is less than 7 per cent of the shell mass.

In the safety of underground burrows, kiwi eggs are less vulnerable to buckling stresses, against which shell mass and thickness presumably evolved. The hatching kiwi has no egg tooth, and no doubt the escape is facilitated by a thin shell.

The Otorohanga Zoological Society's famous X-ray of a female kiwi fifteen hours before laying shows that the egg occupies a large part of the abdominal cavity (see page 169). From records on captive birds, it appears that the 400-gram increase in her body mass is completed as much as a week before the end of the egg-forming cycle. It might be desirable to delay making this burden rigid as long as possible, shortening the period for shell-deposition and resulting in a thin shell. Whether or not this is true, one can appreciate why the hen might decline to eat the day or two before laying. The decrease in body mass over the final two days and laying exceeds the mass of the egg by some 78 grams. This would contain an amount of chemical energy equal to 1.94 days of the hen's standard metabolic rate.

CONCLUSIONS

Although it is grossly oversized by most birds' standards, egg-production by kiwis is not wasteful. Only 57 per cent of the egg's energy stores are expended during embryonic growth and development, permitting advanced precociality, and almost autonomy at hatching. The main difference between kiwi and 'typical' is a shift in timescale of the energy cost of reproduction, a matter of chronology. How much of the adult's foraging is devoted to reproduction before laying or after hatching and at what stage in overall growth is the transition from embryo to neonate accomplished? The female puts more energy into egg-synthesis, her most lavish egg of any bird being laid with enough food to sustain the chick to self-reliance. In absence of the threat of intense predation by mammals, nesting success and chick survival must have been high enough that fewer eggs sufficed. The emphasis could be on 'good value' rather than quantity.

The male performs the long incubation for the advanced development, but at the relaxed pace of a 'kiwi lifestyle'. Record egg and yolk sizes and incubation duration provided an excellent test in the extreme of the Rahn *et al.* model of eggshell function, which linked incubation time and eggshell permeability to oxygen and water vapour. When one variable departs from normal, several other compensatory changes accompany. What may have appeared random is actually very closely programmed by the physical necessity of regulating water loss of the eggshell.

David Lack observed: 'A relatively large egg is advantageous either because it provides the newly hatched chick with a big reserve of food or because it enables the chick to hatch at a later stage of development, but its formation may necessitate a smaller clutch . . .' The oversized egg could have resulted from relaxation of natural selection as smaller descendants appeared from a moa-kiwi lineage. Why didn't the eggs scale down? 'Any system will degenerate to the extent to which there is a relaxation of selective pressures for its maintenance . . . The effectiveness of the environmental strategy arises only as an incidental result of the strategies of other organisms' (G. C. Williams).

Without the threat of mammalian predators, any selective advantage of a large egg could become feasible and allowable. Several kinds of birds — rail, gallinule, duck, parrot — abandoned flight after colonising New Zealand. Why did their eggs all remain in typical proportions to body size of the respective hens? Perhaps because the evolution of large eggs would have entailed such a complex syndrome of other changes that the permutations would approach mathematical improbability. How many mutations would be necessary to lower metabolic rates and temperatures of adults, chicks and eggs, thin the eggshell, doubly reduce the eggshell permeability, and supplement the defences against microbial attack for two and a half months of incubation? The evidence for a downward scaling in body size from the ratite-moa ancestry means that the proto-kiwi did not have to wait for many mutations to get large eggs; their ancestors did that for them in advance.

When an otherwise universal process is missing, we can find valuable insight. Aglomerular teleost fish allowed physiologists to study kidney secretion without confounding effects of filtration, so perhaps the odd kiwis can tell us something about evolutionary scaling and reproductive ecology without complications of mammalian predation and competition. We have a

An X-ray photograph of a female brown kiwi fifteen hours prior to laying an egg. Note that the egg seems to occupy most of the visceral space. The dark cluster in the lower mid-abdomen is the crop with stones therein.
Otorohanga Zoological Society

vested interest in the results of natural experiments seen in the earth's biological diversity and the habitats wherein they occurred, and we are foolish to destroy them.

ACKNOWLEDGEMENTS

An American going to New Zealand with nothing but 'book-learning', some instruments and NSF grant PCM 76-09411 for a sabbatical leave would never have been able to enjoy the mysteries of kiwi biology without the pioneering successes of Barry Rowe, who had the systems designed and running for the first artificial incubation of a kiwi egg. This was, for me, the ultimate in being 'at the right place at the right time', that place being the National Kiwi Centre of the Otorohanga Zoological Society. The technical expertise, logistical support, and hospitality of Barry Rowe, Gilbert Hoffman, Betty Wheeler, Laurie Smith and the other members and staff of the Otorohanga Zoological Society were invaluable and will always be remembered with gratitude and affection. Brian Reid and Colin Roderick of the New Zealand Wildlife Service generously shared their knowledge in several stimulating discussions. C. R. Parr, D. P. Karl, and Robin Whaanga of Ruakura Agricultural Research Centre, provided the bomb calorimetry of egg samples provided by Rowe, Roderick, and Reid, the 'three Rs' of New Zealand Kiwi-ology.

An X-ray photograph of a female brown kiwi 15 hours prior to laying an egg. Note that the egg seems to occupy most of the visceral space. The dark cluster in the lower mid-abdomen is the crop with stones therein.
Otorohanga Zoological Society

KIWIS

BIBLIOGRAPHY

Ar, A. and H. Rahn. 1978. Interdependence of gas conductance, incubation length, and weight of the avian egg. In: J. Pijper (ed.), *Respiratory Function in Birds, Adult and Embryonic*. Spring-Verlag, Berlin.

Ar, A. and H. Rahn. 1980. Water in the avian egg: overall budget of incubation. *Amer. Zool.* 20: 373–84.

Ar, A., H. Rahn, and C. V. Paganelli. 1979. The avian egg: mass and strength. *Condor* 81: 331–7.

Ar, A. and Y. Yom Tov. 1978. The evolution of parental care in birds. *Evolution* 32: 655–69.

Aschoff, J. and H. Pohl. 1970. Rhythmic variations in energy metabolism. *Fed. Proc.* 29: 1541–52.

Board, R. G. 1982. Properties of avian egg shells and their adaptive value. *Biol. Rev.* 57: 1–28.

Board, R. G. and D. J. Hornsey. 1978. Plasma and egg white proteins. In: A. H. Brush (ed.), *Chem. Zool.* Vol X: *Aves*. Academic Press. N.Y.

Board, R. G. and S. G. Tullett. 1977. An arbitrary classification of the pore systems in avian eggshells. *J. Zool.* (London) 182: 251–65.

Bock, W. 1963. The cranial evidence for ratite affinities. *Proc. Inter. Ornithol. Congr.* 13: 39–54.

Body, D. R. and Reid, B. 1983. The lipid and amino acid composition of the kiwi (*Apteryx australis mantelli*) ratite eggs. *J. Sci. Food Agric.* 34: 587–92.

Brody, S. 1945. *Bioenergetics and Growth.* Hafner, New York.

Calder, W. A. 1978a. The kiwi. *Sci. Amer.* (1) 239: 132–42.

Calder, W. A. 1978b. The kiwi: a case of compensating divergences from allometric predictions. In: J. Pijper (ed.), *Respiratory Function in Birds, Adult and Embryonic*. Spring-Verlag, Berlin.

Calder, W. A. 1979. The kiwi and egg design: evolution as a package deal. *Bioscience* 29: 461–7.

Calder, W. A. 1984. *Size, Function, and Life History*. Harvard Univ. Press, Cambridge, Mass.

Calder, W. A. 1985. Size. In: B. Campbell, E. Lack (eds.), *A Dictionary of Birds*. T. & A. D. Poysner, Calton, England.

Calder, W. A. and T. J. Dawson. 1978. Resting metabolic rates of ratite birds: the kiwi and the emu. *Comp. Biochem. Physiol.* 60A: 479–81.

Calder, W. A. and J. R. King. 1974. Thermal and caloric relations of birds. In: D. S. Farner and J. R. King (eds.), *Avian Biology*, Vol. 4. Academic Press, N.Y.

Calder, W. A., C. R. Parr, and D. R. Carl. 1978. Energy content of eggs of the brown kiwi *Apteryx australis*: an extreme in avian evolution. *Comp. Biochem. Physiol.* 60A: 177–79.

Cracraft, J. 1974. Phylogeny and evolution of the ratite birds. *Ibis* 116: 494–521.

deBoer, L. E. M. 1980. Do the chromosomes of the kiwi provide evidence for a monophyletic origin of the ratites? *Nature* 287: 84–5.

Drent, R. 1975. Incubation. In: D. S. Farner and J. R. King (eds.), *Avian Biology*, Vol. 5. Academic Press, N.Y.

Farner, D. S., N. Chivers, and T. Rinez. 1956. The body temperatures of the North Island kiwis. *Emu* 56: 199–206.

Frazer, J. F. D. 1977. Growth of young vertebrates in the egg or uterus. *J. Zool.* Lond. 183: 189–201.

Garland, T. Jr. and R. B. Huey. 1987. Testing symmorphosis: does structure match functional requirements? *Evolution* 41: 1404–9.

Gould, S. J. 1966. Allometry and size in ontogeny and phylogeny. *Biol. Rev.* 41: 487–640.

Gould, S. J. 1986. Of kiwi eggs and the liberty bell. *Natural History* 11/86: 20–9.

Hoyt, D. F., D. Vleck and C. M. Vleck. 1978. Metabolism of avian embryos: ontogeny and temperature effects in the ostrich. *Condor* 80: 265–71.

Huxley, J. S. 1927. On the relation between egg-weight and body-weight in birds. *J. Linnean Soc.* (Zool.) 36: 457–466.

Huxley, J. S. 1932. *Problems of Relative Growth.* Methuen, London, (republished 1972 by Dover, New York).

Kinsky, F. C. 1971. The consistent presence of paired ovaries in the kiwi (*Apteryx*) with some discussion of this condition in other birds. *J. Ornithol.* 112: 334–57.

Lack, D. 1968. *Ecological Adaptations for Breeding in Birds.* Methuen, London.

Laird, A. K. 1966. Dynamics of embryonic growth. *Growth* 30: 263–75.

Lasiewski, R. C. and W. R. Dawson. 1967. A re-examination of the relation between standard metabolic rate and body weight in birds. *Condor* 69: 12–23.

Lindstedt, S. L. and J. H. Jones. 1987. Symmporphosis: the concept of optimal design. In: M. E. Feder, A. F. Bennett, W. W. Burggren, and R. B. Huey (eds.), *New Directions in Ecological Physiology*. Cambridge Univ. Press, Cambridge, England.

McLennan, J. A. 1988. Breeding of North Island brown kiwi, *Apteryx australis mantelli*, in Hawke's Bay, New Zealand. *NZ J. Ecology* 11: 89–97.

Nathusius, W. V. 1871. Uber die Eischalen von Aepyornis, Dinornis, Apteryx und einigen Crypturiden. *Z. wiss. Zool.* 21: 330–55.

Olson, S. L. 1983. The fossil record of birds. In: D. S. Farner and J. R. King (eds.), *Avian Biology*, Vol. VIII. Academic Press, Orlando, Florida.

Osuga, D. T., and R. E. Feeney. 1968. Biochemistry of the egg-white protein of the ratite group. *Arch. Biochem. and Biophys.* 124: 560–74.

Paganelli, C. V., A. Olszowka and A. Ar. 1974. The avian egg: surface area, volume, and density. *Condor* 76: 319–25.

Parkes, K. C. 1975. Special review. *Auk* 92: 818–30.

Pennycuick, C. J. 1972. *Animal Flight*. Edward Arnold, London.

Peters, R. H. 1983. *The Ecological Implications of Body Size*. Cambridge Univ. Press, Cambridge, England.

Prager, E. M., A. C. Wilson, and N. Armheim. 1974. Widespread distribution of lysozyme g in egg white of birds. *Biol. Chem.* 249: 7295–7.

Prager, E. M., A. C. Wilson, D. T. Osuga, and R. E. Feeney. 1976. Evolution of flightless land birds on southern continents: transferrin comparison shows monophyletic origin of ratites. *J. Mol. Evol.* 8: 283–94.

Rahn, H. and A. Ar. 1974. The avian egg: incubation time and water loss. *Condor* 76: 147–52.

Rahn, H. and A. Ar. 1980. Gas exchange of the avian egg: time, structure, and function. *Amer. Zool.* 20: 477–84.

Rahn, H., A. Ar, and C. V. Paganelli. 1979. How bird eggs breathe. *Sci. Amer.* 240(2): 46–55.

Reid, B. 1971a. The weight of the kiwi and its egg. *Notornis* 18: 245–9.

Reid, B. 1971b. Composition of a kiwi egg. *Notornis* 18: 250–2.

Reid, B. 1972. North Island brown kiwi: *Apteryx australis mantelli*. Measurements and weight of a young chick. *Notornis* 19: 261–6.

Reid, B. 1977. The energy value of the yolk reserve in a North Island brown kiwi chick (*Apteryx australia mantelli*) *Notoruis* 24: 194–5.

Reid, B., and G. R. Williams. 1975. The kiwi. In: G. Kuschel (ed.), *Biogeography and Ecology in New Zealand*. D. W. Junk, The Hague.

Ricklefs, R. E. 1974. Energetics of reproduction in birds. In: R. A. Payneter, Jr. (ed.), *Avian Energetics*. Nuttall Ornithology Club, Publ. No. 15, Cambridge, MA.

Ricklefs, R. E. 1977. Composition of eggs of several bird species. *Auk*. 94: 350–6.

Romanoff, A. L. and A. J. Romanoff, 1949. *The Avian Egg*. J. Wiley and Sons, N.Y.

Rowe, B. 1978. Incubation temperatures of the North Island brown kiwi (*Apteryx australis mantelli*). *Notornis* 25: 213–17.

Rowe, B. and W. A. Calder. 1978. Artificial incubation of a North Island brown kiwi. *Internat. Zoo Yearbook*, Vol 18.

Schmidt-Nielsen, K. 1984. *Scaling: Why is Animal Size so Important?* Cambridge Univ. Press, Cambridge, England.

Seymour, R. S. and R. A. Ackerman. 1980. Adaptations to underground nesting in birds and reptiles. *Amer. Zool.* 20: 437–47.

Silyn-Roberts, H. 1983. The pore geometry and structure of the eggshell of the North Island brown kiwi, *Apteryx australis mantelli*. *J. Microscopy* 130: 23–36.

Silyn-Roberts, H. and R. M. Sharp. 1985. Preferred orientation of calcite in the ratite and tinamou eggshells. *J. Zool. Lond.* A205: 39–52.

Sotherland, P. R. and H. Rahn. 1987. On the composition of bird eggs. *Condor* 89: 48–65.

Stearns, S. C. 1976. Life history tactics: a review of the ideas. *Q. Rev. Biol.* 51: 3–47.

Taylor, C. R. and E. R. Weibel. 1981. Design of the mammalian respiratory system. I. Problem and strategy. *Resp. Physiol.* 44: 1–10.

Tyler, C. and K. Simkiss. 1959. A study of the egg shells of ratite birds. *Proc. Zool. Soc.* London: 133: 200–43.

Vleck, C. M., D. F. Hoyt and D. J. Vleck. 1979. Metabolism of avian embryos: patterns in altricial and precocial birds. *Physiol. Zool.* 52: 363–77.

Vleck, C. M., D. Vleck and D. F. Hoyt. 1980. Patterns of metabolism and growth in avian embryos. Amer. Zool. 20: 405–16.

Vleck, D. J. 1978. Allocation of egg energy stores in the ostrich, rhea, and emu. In: The Energetics of Activity and Growth, Doctoral dissertation. University of California, Los Angeles.

Wenzel, B. M. 1971. Olfactory sensation in the kiwi and other birds. *Annals of the New York Academy of Sciences* 188: 183–93.

Williams, G. C. 1966. *Adaptation and Natural Selection*. Princeton University Press, Princeton, New Jersey.

Williams, G. R. 1973. Birds. In: G. R. Williams (ed.), *The Natural History of New Zealand: An Ecological Survey*. A. H. & A. W. Reed, Wellington.

Wolf, E. C. 1988. Avoiding a mass extinction of species. In: L. Starke (ed.), *State of the World 1988*. W. W. Norton, New York.

raymond ching

11

THE KIWI IN ART

A consideration of the kiwi as a subject for art would not, until now, have been valid. Indeed, the idea of any wild animal as a serious subject of Western art has not previously been entertained. Animals have been included in paintings, representing man's wealth or occupation or knowledge. They have been acceptable as a subject of sporting art or illustrating a scientific treatise, but it is only with the dawning realisation that they are disappearing that animals have become a subject of serious artistic consideration in themselves. With our understanding that wild animals are essential to the well-being of the human species — both physically and spiritually — their art status is changing.

Until Ray Harris-Ching's first paintings of the kiwi were completed in the late 1960s ('The Gumdigger's Waistcoat' is typical), the bird had not been painted seriously as a central subject. By the late 1970s, Harris-Ching had developed a personal vision of these birds, quite unlike anything earlier seen. The results form the basis of this book; the birds live and breathe and have real presence on the page. It is clear now that kiwis can be the subject of art, and it is of interest to follow the progress of their emergence from their first representation by talented illustrators of the nineteenth century.

From the earliest attempts to the present time, the portrayal of kiwis in a two-dimensional plane has presented problems for both illustrators and artists. The bird does not easily fit into the illustrative formula devised by the careful analysis of study-skins for size, pattern and colour, or incorporation into a body-shape form that was known to be similar. There is no other bird like the kiwi, and so the illustrator who had never seen one alive had no similar taxonomy on which to base his work.

The greatest of these illustrators is J. G. Keulemans. Neither before nor since he made the beautiful plates to accompany the text for Part I of J. D. Rowley's *Ornithological Miscellany* (1875) has the kiwi been so perfectly represented in ornithological literature. In a century where fine bird books reached their pinnacle, no illustrator so dominated the field as Keulemans, and nowhere did he better portray kiwis than in the Rowley work. These glorious plates remain the most aesthetically satisfying of all kiwi illustrations and were quite superior to his earlier work, commissioned by Walter Buller for his monumental *History of the Birds of New Zealand* (1872).

John Gerard Keulemans was born in Rotterdam in 1842 and spent early years working at the Leyden Museum, where he mastered lithography under the patronage of Hermann Schlegal. The dominance of London's Zoological Society in the field of ornithological publications drew him to England, where he remained until his death in 1912. His ability to transfer his own drawings directly to the lithographic stone gives his work an aesthetic edge

'The Gumdigger's Waistcoat', North Island brown kiwi, by Ray Harris-Ching. Oil on panel, 1969.

over most of his contemporaries; he was able to retain the subtleties almost always lost at another's hand.

Keulemans' plates of species other than kiwis for Buller's book remain amongst the very finest of their kind. His representation of the huia, tui, kokako, stitch-bird, etc., were, at publication, amongst Keulemans' best work and remain the most perfect set of illustrations yet undertaken of the birds of these islands.

Little spotted kiwi, *Apteryx owenii*. Hand-coloured lithograph by J. G. Keulemans from G. D. Rowley's *Ornithologial Miscellany* (London, 1875–78).

Brown kiwi chick. Hand-coloured lithograph by J. G. Keulemans from G. D. Rowley's *Ornithological Miscellany* (London, 1875–78).

Little spotted kiwi chick. Hand-coloured lithograph by J. G. Keulemans from G. D. Rowley's *Ornithological Miscellany* (London, 1875–78).

J. G. Keulemans, *c.* 1880.

KIWIS

There were, we now know, some errors in the detailing of a number of species: (most particularly, the wattles on the kokako are not accurate to life), but our knowledge of these very specific visual details had not much further advanced until Geoff Moon published his colour photographs in *New Zealand Birds* in the early 1970s, revealing the truth of the intense blue, plastic-like wattles and forever changing our perspective of these birds. More than one hundred years earlier, Keulemans had no such information and was obliged to rely on available knowledge, laid over the formula he had evolved to accommodate all bird species — even those never seen alive by him — and by the careful analysis of study-skins, as earlier described.

For example, the now extremely rare black robin, *Petroica traversi*, from the Chatham Islands, whilst unique to that area, has close and readily available relatives as a reference source flourishing nearby in Australia in the scarlet robin, *Petroica multicolour*, flame robin, *Petroica phoenicca*, and rose robin, *Petroica rosea*. For the illustrator, all of these birds make more or less the same shape. With the study-skin specimen as a guide, the differing colours and patterns are painted onto the basic form.

So it was not especially necessary for nineteenth-century illustrators to see each and every bird alive before preparing their plate (indeed, most illustrators would have seen hardly any of the birds they were asked to draw), and Keulemans was no exception.

We are easily able to see that his first plates of kiwis, those for Walter Buller, don't fit the 'formula' and are consequently less satisfactory than other plates in the book. How cleverly Keulemans persuades us that his portrayal of hitherto-unseen birds, such as fernbird or kea, is entirely true and correct, but how less convinced we are with the kiwi plates. Here are birds so out of the ordinary, so unexpected, so improbable, that convention and formula fail him. The birds this time are not interchangeable with anything else, and his lack of conviction is apparent. Here he is asked to draw birds that have no keel bones to hold flight muscles, with legs set unexpectedly far back to accommodate an unusual form of locomotion, and, most baffling of all for the illustrator, their feathers do not lie in tracts.

For most birds, the feathers grow in rows of a predictable pattern, but with kiwis, growth is much more like mammal fur or human hair. The feathers lie and move in ways not usual for birds, and Keulemans is at first ill at ease with this unexpected circumstance. However, with the publication of Rowley's *Miscellany* just a few years after the Buller work, the great illustrator shows he has resolved any uncertainties in a series of five, totally satisfying plates — each as beautiful as the other.

Earlier in the century, J. Werner produced a painting of the North Island brown kiwi, to be engraved and reproduced by Dumont d'Urville in his *Voyage au Pôle Sud*. Signed and dated 1843, this beautiful watercolour shows all the characteristics of a work produced by an artist directly from a preserved specimen and not to any illustrator's formula.

Usually, works from such an early date are stylised fabrications, although often no less attractive for their formalised view. The plate by H. C. Richter and John Gould from *Birds of Australia* (1848) is an example — and the same characteristics are evident in the earlier brown kiwi plate by Elizabeth Gould for the same work.

Here are birds drawn onto lithographic stone by the use of a crayon, setting a style that would dominate natural history publishing for the rest of the century. The differences between Werner's approach and that of the Gould works are fundamental and persist to the present: either the artist or illustrator draws what he *sees*, or he draws what he *knows to be there.*

North Island brown kiwi, *Apteryx australis mantelli*. Hand-coloured engraving from a painting by J. Werner for Dumont d'Urville's *Voyage au Pôle Sud* (Paris, 1842–54).

B

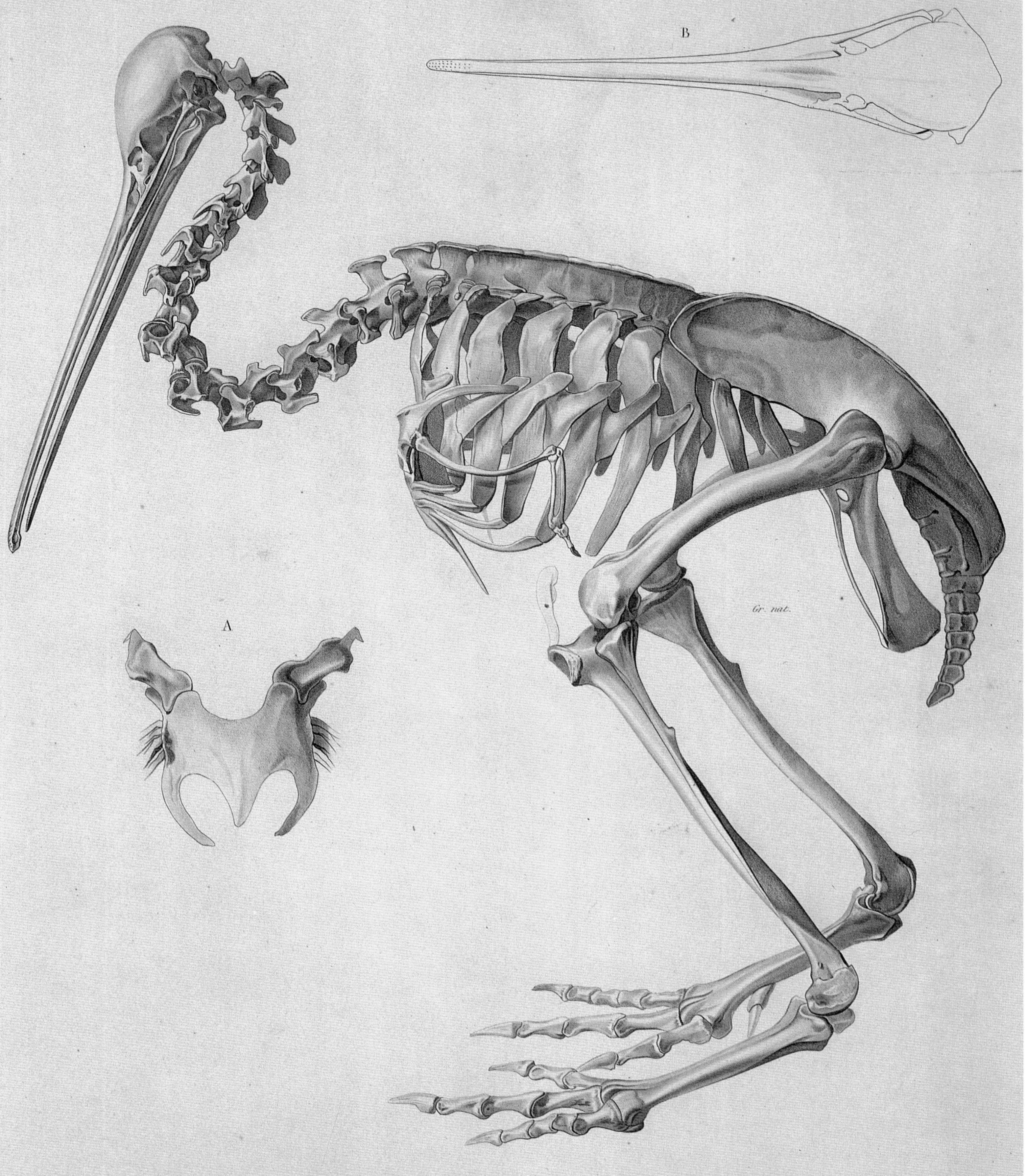

B

A

Gr. nat.

Dessiné par Werner. Dirigé par Borromée. Gravé par Baron.

APTERYX AUSTRAL. (Shaw)

Gide Editeur. Impr. de Bougeard.

Brown kiwi, *Apteryx australis*. Hand-coloured lithograph by Elizabeth Gould from J. Gould's *Birds of Australia* (London, 1840–69).

Richter and Gould's kiwis are quite clearly constructed to a formula based on assumptions that bird species within their family will make similar shapes that may, once identified, be followed with some assurance, even for a bird not observed alive.

This position allows the portrayal of any species from just the possession of a specimen skin. The colours and patterns are duly noted from the skin and then laid onto the body shape already formulated. The results of such a method are, at their best, very pleasing indeed, and surprisingly accurate, but at their least, quickly become repetitive and even tedious.

On the other hand, the preparation of the watercolour painting by Werner shows no signs of formula; the bird is quite clearly drawn and painted direct from the specimen — in this case either a fully preserved body or a carefully prepared study-skin. There can be no mistaking this, for the detailing, most especially about its head and neck, cannot be painted in any other way. The patterns have been drawn because they have been seen by the artist, right then, as he works. They are not assumed to be there — what is drawn is what is seen. The resulting painting — a work made up of numerous first-hand observations, specific to this one occasion — is not exactly like anything earlier executed by the artist and not to be repeated in later work.

More than any other, the Prussian Josef Wolf (1820–1899) best bridged the gap between illustration and art in the nineteenth century. Unlike his contemporary Keulemans (a quietly introspective man with few interests outside his illustrative book work), Wolf sought the company of animal artists such as Edwin Landseer. After his move to London in 1848, his works were prized both as scientific illustrations and for their value as original paintings.

Skeleton of a kiwi. Engraving from a drawing by J. Werner for Dumont d'Urville's *Voyage au Pôle Sud* (Paris, 1842–54).

KIWIS

The small pencil study of brown kiwis reproduced here shows very well this unusual marrying of two disciplines: the birds are shown precisely and accurately to meet the requirements of scientists, but bathed in light and with such convincing form as to satisfy, too, the aesthetic eye.

Throughout the nineteenth century and for much of the twentieth, the kiwi is represented as a subject of man's knowledge — or status, when skinned and in the form of a cloak, and seen about the shoulders of Maori chiefs. A particularly fine and convincing rendering of the texture of kiwi feathers is in the portrait of Tawhiao Matutaera Potatau Te Wherowhero, an impressive painting undertaken in 1885 by Gottfried Lindauer. With a spirit and technique always inferior to that of New Zealand's great master painter of the Maori, C. F. Goldie, Lindauer nonetheless produced a series of paintings depicting various aspects of Maori life that often include well-painted details of kiwi plumage.

With just the rarest of exceptions then, painted images of kiwis have been confined to illustrations for bird books where, for much of the nineteenth century, numerous engravings appeared in works, great and small, as the bird became more generally known to science and a curious public throughout Europe.

'Tawhiao Matutaera Potatau Te Wherowhero' by G. Lindauer, *c.* 1885. Commissioned by Sir Walter Buller for the London Exhibition of 1886.
Courtesy of the Wanganui Museum

Brown kiwis. Pencil drawing highlighted with white, by Joseph Wolf, *c.* 1870.
Courtesy of the Zoological Society of London

THE KIWI IN ART

In the late 1930s, with the advent of reasonably inexpensive colour printing, the Forest and Bird Protection Society of New Zealand commissioned Lilly A. Daff to prepare a series of watercolour paintings for a volume proposed to popularise native birds and make information on them more generally accessible. The Daff paintings found a place among the images of their time, and, although her work has probably been overtaken by more sophisticated views, her plates of kiwis still have their own charm, unmistakable and not quite like any other.

A living kiwi as the central subject to a painting was absent from art of any distinction, until now, in the last decades of the twentieth century. The reasons for its virtual absence in art to date are entirely in keeping with the complex set of thoughts that have excluded wild birds generally from figuring as art. But our view of the responsibilities and place we hold on our planet is changing, and with this comes a change in our perception of subjects worthy of our art attention.

It is clear from the Harris-Ching works in this book that kiwis are no longer seen as stylised products of the illustrator's formula. These birds are at last the subject of art; although in them we may learn further of the birds, we also learn more of ourselves and the things we hold most dear.

North Island brown kiwi, *A. a. mantelli*.
Watercolour by L. A. Daff.
Courtesy of the Royal Forest and Bird Protection Society of New Zealand

Index